COVENANT OF TRUTH

BRITH EMETH

My Jewish Roots

My Jewish Roots

by

S o l o m o n   S i m o n

Translated from the Yiddish by Shlomo Katz

Philadelphia

The Jewish Publication Society of America

1956 · 5716

Library of Congress Catalog Card No.: 56-7783

PRINTED IN THE UNITED STATES OF AMERICA

To

MAURICE SAMUEL

*whose roots are firm
in Jewish life and lore*

Contents

My Jewish Roots.

The town was ringed by forests and scores of peasant villages. No sooner did one leave the last house behind, than one entered a vast and alien world. Yet the town was not submerged in this alien world. Some hundreds of Jewish families lived in the town, and they were like a sovereign kingdom with its own laws and customs which everyone observed, though there was no authority to enforce them.

It was a town of shoemakers and tailors, teamsters and coachmen, storekeepers and peddlars. Outwardly, they were merely some hundreds of families in a remote corner of Polesyeh near the Minsk swamps. Yet this impoverished community possessed immense resources of the spirit.

Wherever Jews live one can find reincarnations of these small-town Jews, who seemed so pitiful and pedestrian in their everyday life, but who were in truth far from pitiful, and who, in the midst of their small daily cares, cherished a deep knowledge that they had made a covenant with God to bear the burden of His Law—that He was their Father and they were His children.

They accumulated great treasures of the spirit which sustain us to this day.

This is the story of one of that town's sons.

1. *One of Eight*

Shimon was the fourth child in a family of eight. They came in this order: Gitte and Simcha, Rochel-Leah and Shimon, Breine and Shlomo, Elke and Binyomin. Their Mother often said: "I brought my children into the world as one plaits a braid: this way a girl, that way a boy. Always a girl first, and then a boy, I short-changed neither side. I gave an even number of both."

All the children except Shimon were healthy and sound in mind and in body. Only he was not up to par. He suffered from rickets—"the English disease," as they called it—and his legs would not hold him up. He was a *sidun*—a sitter. No doctor was consulted. Why bother? The child would outgrow his ailment, the family said.

The first thing that Shimon remembers is terror. Because he always sat on the floor and could not even crawl on all fours, he was afraid. He reasoned that the table, the chairs, the kitchen bench could all walk, because they stood upright. But he could not walk, so he had to beware of them. Should they take it into their heads to start walking, it would be necessary to make way for them, to move aside; but he could not run away from them; his situation was desperate.

At dusk all the objects in the house loomed bigger, thick with shadows. The boy looked up to the red table and saw it flex its thick legs. It would start walking any minute.

3

The chairs arranged around the table were pushing it. Shimon knew that he had to move aside. He made great efforts to stand on all fours and to scamper away. But neither hands nor feet obeyed him. He stretched out on the floor and rolled into a corner. There he sat up again. He felt the wall hard and cool against his back and knew that he could move no farther. He stared into the deepening darkness of the room. Now the table could no longer be seen distinctly, and Shimon was convinced that it was walking about somewhere in the gloom. Soon it would come to his corner and step on him with its chunky legs and crush him. He must save himself. He must call Mother to his rescue. She would come and place him on the sofa. The ailing boy screamed wildly: "Mama!"

Mother was accustomed to these outcries. She would rush in and light the lamp, meantime blaming herself: "Woe is me! Again I forgot and left him alone in the dark! Don't I know that he is afraid of the dark?" She would find him crouching in his corner and lift him to the sofa. She was a slight, emaciated woman, and Shimon was already a boy of three and a half, and heavy for her to lift. She would then sit with him on the sofa and hug him to herself.

But Shimon would not be calmed easily. Sobs would shake his childish body even as Mother's hand caressed his hair. And in her heart she protested to God: "What have I done to deserve this? The child is not only an invalid— his brain, too, seems to be clouded."

She would not say this aloud, knowing how strangely responsive the child was to her slightest moods. Aloud she encouraged him: "There, now, you have nothing to fear; Mother is with you, my little bird." But the cheer in her voice found no echo in her heart, which wept and implored: "God! Have mercy on me and on him! I am a sinful woman, but I do not deserve such punishment!"

The dawns terrified Shimon even more. His Father, Ben-Zion the shoemaker, was a poor provider, and Mother had to operate a bakery to supplement his earnings. She would

4

rise before dawn and start a fire in the oven; then she would knead the dough for the bread, rolls and beigel. When the fire in the oven was in full blast, she would rouse the older children, Gitte, Simcha and Rochel-Leah. But Shimon would awaken as soon as Mother left her bed. He slept on the long couch, with his head near the door to the kitchen, and watched her every move.

Now she is in the kitchen, removing the wooden "door" from the oven's mouth. She stacks the cut logs in the oven and places thin, dry kindling under them. But the heavy chunks do not surrender to the flames so easily. Here a piece of bark catches fire, there a splinter. The rest of the wood is brightly lit by the flames, but does not catch on. The kindling flares and crackles. The sawed-off ends of the logs begin to hiss and to sweat big, bubbly gobs of moisture. Shimon watches the flames as they envelop the bulky chunks of wood. He is sure the logs want to run away but cannot because they have no hands or feet. The flames grow bigger and brighter and merge into one great fire that crackles gaily. Now the large pieces of wood have caught on and the big flame crowds into the black chimney and cannot get into it. Large sheets of flame break off and leap into the kitchen.

Shimon watches the play of the fire and shudders. It seems so aggressive. Any minute now and it will engulf the entire house. Everybody will run away; but not he, because his legs don't support him, and he will burn up, together with the couch, and the mattress stuffed with straw on which he sleeps, and the quilt and the pillow. He hides his head under the pillow so as not to see the fire, but with his head covered he feels hot and cannot breathe. Now he is sure that the fire has leaped out of the oven, and he is terrified. He begins to whimper and then to cry softly. No one hears him, so he makes a great outcry to call attention to himself.

Mother responds from the kitchen: "My misfortune! You're at it again!"

5

"I am afraid!" Shimon screams.

"It's not dark in the house. What are you afraid of now?"

"I'm afraid of the fire in the oven!"

Mother spits on the floor three times and intones: "May all the evil dreams that I dreamed this night and the night before and the year before this befall my enemies and come to pass in fallow fields and dark forests! Have you ever heard of such a thing? Afraid of the fire in the oven! Should I stop baking because of you? And what will we eat? Out of your father's big earnings?"

Shimon knows that Mother is right, but his fear of the fire does not leave him. She is safe, because she can always run away. But what will he do in case the fire engulfs the house?

Mother now comes to his sofa and talks to him as one talks to an adult. "So what should I do?" she asks. "Your legs are bad, but there is nothing the matter with your head, and you are a great talker; so, tell me, what is it you are afraid of?"

"You won't leave me if you have to run away from the fire?" Shimon pleads.

Mother is startled by the question and looks at him in wonder. She realizes that something strange which she cannot comprehend is going on in the child's mind. She promises readily: "No, I won't leave you. You are a big boy and too heavy for me to carry, but I will see to it that Simcha carries you."

Shimon is reassured.

Shimon is nearly five and a half years old and still cannot walk. But he can crawl around and has lost many of his terrors. His speech is like that of an adult. He knows all the benedictions one recites over different kinds of food; he knows the *Modeh Ani* which is recited on waking, and he can say the special grace for children: *Blessed be the Merciful, the King of the world, to Whom this bread belongs.*

6

Whatever he hears stays fixed in his memory, and he often amazes the family by repeating verbatim something that he had heard, or singing a song exactly as he had heard it rendered. But the trouble with him is that he believes literally everything that he hears. At night, especially, the tales he hears during the day acquire reality and are embellished by his imagination. This causes him much grief. A source of great terror at this time were the rumblings and whistlings of the locomotives at dawn.

Beyond the house extended vegetable gardens which gradually gave way to the Polesyeh swamps and a pine forest. The railroad and the station were on the other side of the woods. Three times a day a train stopped at the station, and an hour before the arrival of each train the station master would start his complicated maneuvers to clear the main track of empty cars that always somehow managed to be in the wrong place.

The switch engine which shunted the long strings of empty cars hissed and rumbled and whistled. Its whistling, in particular, was deafening. During the day, other noises drowned it out to some extent. But in the evening, and especially before dawn, it was extremely penetrating.

Shimon had never seen a train and could not visualize the source of the constant and ear-splitting whistles that came from beyond the swamps. He would lie in bed and listen: one long blast, then four short ones, then another prolonged one. And this would be repeated again and again.

Shimon decided that a devil was the cause of all these sounds, a devil who made his home in the swamps. He visualized the devil as a huge dog, as big as a calf, with a chimney-like head. In addition to his four legs the devil had three arms and a single eye in the middle of his forehead. At night the devil wandered about the grass and brush that covered the swamps, fishing and hunting animals that strayed from farms. But as soon as the devil sensed that day was approaching, he would frantically seek some place to hide in during the day. Then he would rear

on his hind legs, stretch his three clenched fists heaven-
ward, and howl at the moon.

With bated breath Shimon listened to the piercing shriek
from beyond the swamp. He shivered at the thought that
the devil might lose his head and rush toward the houses,
and in that case Shimon's house would be the first he would
enter, because it stood right next to the fence. He began
wondering whether the *mezuzahs* had been checked recently. Then it occurred to him that a devil could also
enter through a window, just as the soul of a dying man
floated out through a window.

A cold sweat broke out on his body at this thought, and
his teeth chattered with fright. He would control his fear
as long as he could, and then begin whimpering softly and
finally he could no longer restrain himself and would burst
out crying.

With a bang Mother would put away her poker in a
corner and go to the boy's couch. "Well? What is it now?"

"Why don't we have *mezuzahs* on the windows?"

Mother stared in amazement. "What are you saying?"

"*Mezuzahs* on the windows, to keep the devil out of the
house."

Mother's arms hung helplessly. She wanted to scold him,
but changed her mind and sat down near him. "Shame on
you, Shimon," she said. "You are a big boy now. You can
recite the *Modeh Ani* and all the blessings, yet you are
afraid of a devil. Why don't you think of God? That's what
I want to know. Don't you think He sees everything? Do
you think He would leave us unprotected? You say *Modeh
Ani* when you get up, and you recite a blessing before you
eat, and you say grace after eating—so why are you afraid?
You think a devil can do anything he pleases? You think
he can go wherever he likes without God's permission?
Ours is a Jewish home, with *mezuzahs* on the doors and a
full shelf of sacred books. Now go back to sleep, I have to
return to the oven."

Shimon would feel persuaded by Mother's arguments. He

8

still wanted to ask her why the devil made such awful noises in the swamp, but was ashamed. Reassured, he would fall asleep again.

The curtain of gloomy memories suddenly parts in Shimon's mind. Gone are the frightening twilights and the terror-filled dawns of childhood. Instead, there comes to his mind the remembrance of a bright, late summer afternoon. The sun is already low in the sky and its warmth is gentle. Shimon plays with his sister Rochel-Leah, who is two years older than he. They play hide-and-seek in a yard cluttered with logs and mounds of boards. The logs are piled high and still have their bark, and the smell of fresh pine sawdust is all over the place. When Shimon climbs up a pile of logs, he can see the entire town and the orchards that ring it.

The two children play hide-and-seek. The piles of logs and boards provide many convenient hiding places. Shimon crouches between some logs and hears his sister searching for him as she sings the customary jingle:

"Sulie maloo
Where are you?"

The idea is to remain still until the seeker gives up, then the hidden one sings out:

"Turn around
And I'll be found!"

Rochel-Leah follows the sound of his voice but Shimon plays a trick on her and scurries away to another pile of logs. She complains bitterly: "You're a cheat! You're a liar." Shimon creeps up behind her and hollers, "Boo." His sister is frightened and clutches her hands to her heart:

"You scared me! You're a liar and you are cruel like a robber. Now I will faint."

Shimon laughs, "You are a silly girl, always fainting."

9

"And you are a 'sitter,' " she taunts him, knowing that this nickname infuriates him.

Shimon does not recall whether they fought that time. He does remember how they ran and skipped home holding hands, and dashed into the house noisily and shouted: "We are hungry!" Mother then gave them baked potato and bread, and cold schav with sour milk and chopped onion. Shimon loudly recited the blessing over the bread, while mother watched and her face glowed with delight: "Thank God, Shimon is now a real boy. God Hearkened to the prayer of a mother's heart."

She sighed softly. Shimon became six years old on the Sabbath after Tisha b'Av, and still did not go to *heder*. But then he only started to walk a week before Shevuos, she apologizes to herself. He will catch up with the others; his wisdom shows on his face.

Shimon recites the children's grace after the meal: *Blessed be the Merciful One* . . . and Mother beams with joy: "Just hear the way he says the words! Perhaps God has at last granted a scholar to the family." Didn't she have enough troubles? She was certainly entitled to some joys too. It wouldn't harm her a bit, she thinks. Her heart beats faster at the thought of having a scholar in the family. So far as she can remember her family could boast only of shoemakers and tailors and coachmen. And now, suddenly, a scholar . . . She wipes her eyes in glad anticipation and her heart pounds swiftly.

2. *Shimon Gets on His Feet*

A few days before Shevuos, Shimon, who was then almost six years old, stood on his feet for the first time, and within a matter of weeks he shot up in height. His protruding belly flattened out; his back straightened and became broader. His complexion, which had been a sickly gray, changed to a healthy tan, and a flush of health now played on his cheeks. His hair became denser and its former dullness gave way to a healthy sheen. Only his eyes did not change and remained as before, wide open and bright blue, and they examined with much wonder and curiosity everything they beheld.

At this stage Shimon became very active and childishly mercurial. He could not stay put for a moment. Speech and laughter constantly tumbled from his mouth, and his hands were ever busy.

"He is trying to catch up on lost time," Mother said. "For almost six years he couldn't even crawl, so now he is in a hurry to make up for it."

At this time Shimon no longer cried, and lost all his fears. Now Mother complained that he had lost all sense of fear.

One Friday afternoon Shimon tried to join the bigger boys as they played in the yard. His advances were rudely repulsed. "Go away, 'sitter,' where are you shoving," they jeered, scarcely paying any attention to him.

Shimon resented the indignity. "Oh, yeh! You can only jump over fences or walk on your hands, but I can jump off the stable roof," he boasted.

Boruch-Leibe, the carpenter's son, who was the leader of the gang, mocked him: "Look who is talking! Can't even walk right and wants to jump from a roof!"

Shimon's older brother, Simcha, came to his assistance: "Leave him alone. Pick on someone your own size."

But Boruch wouldn't desist: "I hate boasters. A peanut like him and he says he'll jump from the roof."

Shimon listened to this exchange and stared defiantly at Boruch. "I have already jumped from the roof," he declared challengingly.

"When?"

"When nobody was looking."

"Hear that?" Boruch jeered. "He sings without a sound; he jumps when no one is around."

The boys caught up the taunt and flung it at Shimon, repeating it in a sing-song.

Shimon faced the boys. He felt alone, one against many. His lips twitched as if he was about to cry, but he did not cry. Instead he announced: "O.K., I'll show you."

And he ran to the stable and started climbing up the wall, where the protruding logs gave him a foothold.

"Don't!" his brother Simcha warned him. "Get down before you fall and hurt yourself." But Shimon did not answer and clambered upward. Terrified, Simcha ran home to call Mother.

When Simcha returned with Mother on the run, they found Shimon standing on the ground, surrounded by the admiring crowd of boys. He was pale, but a triumphant smile played on his face. "Did he really jump from the roof?" Mother kept asking. "Did he really jump?"

"He jumped!" the boys outshouted each other. "We saw him do it. He landed on his feet, just like he had springs in his legs."

Mother silently led him home. She wanted to give him

a good spanking, but her hands somehow refused to obey her. As soon as she got him into the house her anger exploded in a torrent of protest:

"Now what kind of devils have gotten into you—that's what I would like to know. Only a while ago you were afraid of a table and a chair, the fire in the oven and the whistle of an engine, and God only knows what else. Everything frightened you. You wanted *mezuzahs* on the windows—nothing less would quiet your fears. You trembled before every imagined thing. And suddenly you aren't afraid to jump from roofs! Now what kind of devils got into you—that's what I would like to know."

Shimon calmly gazed at her as the words tumbled from her lips and an innocent smile wrinkled his face. Mother noticed his smile first, then she became aware of the expression in his eyes which was somehow much more mature than his years. The stream of her talk stopped abruptly. A disturbing thought flitted through her head: "He has the mind of an adult; and one never knows what goes on in there. Maybe he is older than his age." But aloud she only said: "You sure can cook up a mess!"

Shimon got into a still worse scrape some six weeks later. Not far from his home, only two orchards away, lived the Deacon of the church. He had a magnificent fruit orchard. His trees always seemed loaded with tempting apples, pears and other fruit. But the orchard was surrounded by a high fence, and as an additional precaution the Deacon kept a huge dog as big as a calf. It was a rare boy who dared trespass the Deacon's guarded precincts.

One bright day in Elul, late in the summer, Shimon climbed the fence of the Deacon's orchard and began picking the windfall apples from under a tree. The Deacon's daughter, Anastasia, who used to come every day to buy fresh beigel from Shimon's mother and could speak Yiddish well, noticed him and came up together with the big dog. Shimon was caught in the act of biting into an apple. He

13

paled slightly but otherwise showed no signs of fear. Anastasia held the dog in check and addressed the six-year-old Shimon in Yiddish:

"Tell me, how does a little boy like you come to steal apples?"

"I wasn't stealing," he answered calmly. "I only took the apples lying on the ground. They are no good. See how rotten they are?" and he pointed to the decayed parts of the apples lying in the grass.

"You know, Shimon," Anastasia stuck to her argument, "when I catch a boy stealing apples, I don't care if it's from the tree or from the ground, I take his cap away and I sick the dog on him."

Shimon nonchalantly bit into the apple he was holding and said: "You're mean. You'd rather have the apples rot than have someone enjoy them."

"You are a smart little Jew," Anastasia laughed, "so this time I'll let you go. But, remember," she pointed a warning finger, "if I am not here the dog will tear you to pieces, and if I catch you a second time I'll sick the dog on you, and he'll tear a chunk out of you and then I will take your cap and your mother will have to buy it back."

Shimon stopped munching his apple. He looked long at Anastasia's cheerful face, her fair hair and her deep blue eyes; then he nodded his head and declared in a tone of resentment: "You are very beautiful and it is a pleasure to look at you. But you are mean."

For an instant Anastasia was confused and did not know what to make of his remark. Here was a boy, still a baby, talking like a man. But her confusion lasted only a moment, and then her laughter rang out so loudly that the dog was scared and began to growl. She sat down on the grass. With one hand she calmed the dog and the other she held to her heart. She laughed and her talk relapsed into Russian which Shimon did not understand: "My God! Hardly old enough to wipe his nose and already knows how to get around a woman. Did you ever hear anything

14

like this! 'You are beautiful so that it's a pleasure to look at you.' If only the older fellows could say such simple sweet things. And just look at the little Jew! A dark little face, and big blue eyes so that one is tempted to kiss him all over. Only yesterday he was a 'sitter' (and this nickname derived from the Russian was the only word that Shimon understood out of her entire outburst) and crawled around in the mud, and now he climbs fences and compliments girls. What a little Jew! Smart as their emperor Solomon."

Shimon stared at her mouth. He realized that what he had told her was somehow very much to her liking. He picked up another juicy apple, wiped it on his sleeve and bit into it. Anastasia calmed down somewhat and again addressed him in Yiddish:

"Here, take a whole bosomful of apples and go. But remember, no more climbing fences. You can get around me with your fine talk, but if you ever come across the dog unattended, you won't get off so lightly."

The following morning, when Anastasia came to buy beigel, she brought a basketful of fruit and gave it to Mehre. "This is for your little Solomon," she said.

"Who is my little Solomon?" Mother wondered.

"Your Shimon, the little 'sitter.' He is a smart little fellow, just like your emperor Solomon in the Bible. But tell him never to climb the fence again or he will get into trouble."

Mother did not understand what it was all about until Anastasia told her the whole story. When the Deacon's daughter left, Mother took Shimon to task. She said: "If it wasn't that for some reason I can't lift a hand against you, I'd beat you black and blue. Oh, if only I'd already live to see the day when you go to heder! God only knows what sort of mischief you will yet get yourself into."

Shimon carelessly listened to his mother; his chief attention was directed toward the basket of fruit. But Mother did not let him off so easily: "It's your luck that the girl

15

has a heart of gold. If it had been the priest's orchard you wouldn't have gotten away whole. His wife or his old maid would have seen to that. And now tell me, how could you risk your life? What would have happened if Anastasia hadn't been there, only the dog?"

Shimon smiled his enigmatic, mature smile, but this only enraged his mother.

"Well, answer me. Why do you risk your life?"

"And will you give me a pear if I do?"

"I will give it to you, but first answer my question."

"Oh, it was nothing. I have been playing with the dog for a long time. He knows me and wouldn't hurt me. And Anastasia is kind. I know her and she knows who I am. She would never sick the dog on me. How could she come to buy beigel if she did? She'd be ashamed. Now give me the pear."

Before this reasoning Mother was helpless. "There is something frightening about his talk," she thought. "Everything so carefully planned in advance. Hardly six years old and talks like an adult." She handed him the pear and reminded him with a sigh: "Recite the blessing."

"I always recite the blessing," Shimon declared calmly. "I am not a Goy."

"You're always in the right," Mother had to admit resent, fully.

Shimon sensed her displeasure. "You want the first bite?" he offered.

Mother looked at him long and steadily, then she nodded her head in resignation: "I don't know whether you are a flatterer or really have a kind heart. All right, I'll take a bite out of your pear."

"Don't forget to say the blessing."

Mother laughed. "There is no getting ahead of you." And she added under her breath: "May you grow in my presence."

16

3. *The Gate to Heaven*

Shimon experienced only one other moment of terror after he learned to walk. This happened when his father brought him to the synagogue the first time.

It was a Saturday morning. Three of them went to the synagogue—the Father, Ben-Zion, the older brother Simcha, and Shimon. For some reason they were late, and by the time they entered the synagogue, Father first, then Simcha, and Shimon trailing behind, the congregation was already immersed in prayer. As soon as they crossed the threshold, Shimon began to retreat. Simcha seized his hand: "Where to?" Shimon turned deathly pale and did not answer. He backed against the wall, as he used to do when he was a little child and was afraid of the dark. He was now shaken by a great fear.

His glance embraced the whole synagogue at once. An entire congregation of men wrapped in prayer shawls stood rocking back and forth. A murmur rose above their heads, but no word was heard distinctly. The murmur rose upward toward the ceiling. But this was not an ordinary ceiling. Painted on it were a sun and its rays, and nestling between the rays were the two tablets.

Shimon's back pressed against the wall and his eyes darted from one figure to another; but in their prayer shawls he could at first recognize no one. Then he identified Michael the grocer. Michael stood near a narrow, high table. He sang something and all the others caught up his tune. Many candles were burning, though it was daylight. And the windows were so huge! And high up on the wall were little windows, and women's faces looked through them.

Simcha tried to drag Shimon to Father's place, but the boy resisted. He felt nailed to the floor. The older boy ran to Father. Father came wrapped in a prayer shawl. He lifted Shimon in his arms and carried him to his seat on the bench facing the Ark which he had inherited from his father. He set Shimon on the bench.

Father saw Shimon's terror and remarked angrily: "Shame on you. Afraid of a Holy Place? Of Jews? You are in a synagogue."

The boy felt ashamed. He looked about himself and gradually began recognizing the familiar faces of neighbors. His fear vanished.

For a long time the synagogue remained a place of wonder for Shimon. At first he was intrigued by the language of the prayers—it was so incomprehensible, yet the words must have a meaning. The words must somehow protect and guard the people who recite them. He wished he could know the meaning of the prayers the way he understood the sense of the benedictions he pronounced. It was true that he did not know the meaning of each word when he recited them, but their general intent was comprehensible to him. He blessed God that he, Shimon, had something to eat: every kind of food called for a different blessing— what he ate thus explained what he recited.

Even then he understood that the words of the prayers were not random, that they had a power to protect and guard against evil. That much he knew. He heard the refrains repeated, exactly the way he did when reciting *Shema* before going to sleep. When he said the *Shema* he believed that God would return to him the soul which he was entrusting into His safekeeping for the night. The

18

prayers in the synagogue must therefore be something of the same sort. They must protect from all kinds of evil. If only he could read the words in the prayer book, he would somehow divine their meaning. But Shimon could not read. All the boys his age could read the prayer book, but not he. There he was, six years old, and still not in heder. The other boys taunted him about it, and his mind was made up—as soon as he started going to heder he would show them what he could do.

But though he could not read the prayer book and did not understand the words he singled out, he loved the Sabbath service, especially when the hazzan halted in the midst of his benediction and the entire congregation intoned, "Blessed is He and blessed is His name," and again when they assented in unison: "Amen." He visualized these responses merging into one huge, round word that floated upward to heaven, after first entering the Holy Ark that was built high into the eastern wall of the synagogue.

The Holy Ark was the gate to heaven. Though he didn't know the Aleph-Bes, Shimon learned to decipher the inscription over the Holy Ark: "This is the gate to God." Eight steps led to the Holy Ark. When one reached the highest step, one could open the doors of the Holy Ark. The Holy Ark was covered by a satin curtain embroidered with two lions. The lions had their mouths wide open, and their tails curled over their backs almost to the open mouths. On Saturdays and holidays the Holy Ark was covered with a silk curtain on which were embroidered in gold thread the two tablets with the ten commandments. Inside the Holy Ark stood the Torahs.

The Torah scroll is holy. If it is carried past, one must kiss it. When one is called up to the Torah one must first recite a benediction. Before reciting the benediction one touches the Torah with the tallis and then kisses the prayer shawl. The Torahs are very holy. The *Shekhinah* hovers over them wherever they are, and the *Shekhinah* also protects the synagogue. All the prayers go into the Holy Ark,

19

which is the gate to heaven, and from there they go directly to God's throne.

Shimon watched and saw the prayers streaming to the Holy Ark. It seemed to him that a haze floated over the heads of the congregation, a haze like the one that hovers over the fields on summer afternoons.

His eyes were fixed in a stare. His brother Simcha, who had just finished the *Shmoneh Esre* (the prayers recited in silence), noticed the strange expression on Shimon's face and nudged him with his elbow:

"Why are you staring there, like a graven image?"

Shimon was roused from his reverie and climbed down from the bench. "Don't you see it?" he asked in a whisper.

"See what?"

"How they flow to the Holy Ark."

"What flows to the Holy Ark?"

"The prayers."

Simcha stared at him with open mouth. "You are crazy," he said. "As I live, you are raving mad."

The hazzan began to intone the *Shmoneh Esre.*

Now Shimon had another nickname: The Nut. But he didn't take it to heart. He was too busy observing everything and ignored the taunts that were flung at him. He made new discoveries. Suddenly he realized that he could remember entire conversations after hearing them only once. The same was true of songs; but he only remembered the words, not the tune.

Though he still didn't go to heder, he discovered that he could learn by heart long fragments of the prayers. He took a great liking to the prayer "Praise the Lord for He is Good, for His mercy endureth forever," especially to the refrain "for His mercy endureth forever" which was repeated after every verse.

When Simcha returned from heder one Friday afternoon, Shimon handed him a prayer book and begged, "Please show me where it says 'Praise the Lord.'"

20

"What do you want to know for, 'sitter'?" Simcha said ungraciously.

"If you will show me the place and point out every line with your finger, I'll show you a trick."

"What trick?"

"You'll see."

"You're kidding."

"I'm not fooling."

"Remember now," Simcha threatened him with a warning finger, "if you fool me, I'll beat the living daylights out of you."

"I'll let you beat me and I won't even cry, if I fool you."

When Shimon talked this way, like a grown-up, Simcha was usually upset and flew into a rage. But this time he restrained himself—he was curious to see the trick he had been promised. He therefore took the prayer book, found the right place in the morning service, and began reading quickly the prayer of praise with its repeated refrains. Shimon halted him: "Not so fast, and we agreed that you point to every line with your finger."

"You drive a hard bargain, and you'd better remember your promise," Simcha warned him, but reduced his speed and read slowly, following the lines with his finger. When he finished he closed the prayer book with finality and said: "Now what's your trick?"

"Read the twenty-six verses once more," Shimon said.

"How do you know there are twenty-six verses?"

"I counted them."

"You counted them?" Simcha couldn't comprehend. "But why should I read them again?"

"You'll see later."

Simcha impatiently reopened the prayer book. "I don't know why I do it," he said irritably, "but remember, if you fool me I'll give you the beating of your life."

"I won't fool you. Now read slowly and follow the lines with your finger."

Simcha repeated his performance. When he finished he

wanted to close the book, but Shimon stopped him. "Don't close the prayer book; I want you to quiz me."

"What do you mean 'quiz you'?"

"See if I know it by heart," Shimon said and, without waiting for an answer, began to recite the prayer word for word. Simcha followed him in the prayer book, and when he had finished, he protested: "You're a liar! You don't know it by heart."

"I'll say it again."

"Go ahead."

Shimon recited it again from memory. The older brother shut the book. He felt a mysterious dread at what he witnessed and could only whisper: "You have an open head." Then, unable to control his fear, he shouted: "Mama! Come here! See what the 'sitter' can do!"

Mother ran out all flustered. "What happened? What?"

"Listen! Just listen," Simcha was excited. "He knows all of 'Praise the Lord' by heart."

Mother and Simcha bent over the prayer book as Shimon repeated the verses by heart. When he finished, Mother felt her knees giving under her and sat down. She wiped her eyes with the corner of her kerchief and mumbled the same words Simcha had said before: "He has an open head, an open brain." Then she spat three times to ward off the evil eye and addressed Simcha: "Don't you dare touch him, do you hear?"

"Who is bothering him? It's me that's afraid of him," Simcha defended himself.

Mother sighed. Perhaps God had granted her a scholar? If only she would live to see the day when he started going to heder.

4. *The New Synagogue*

The town had three synagogues that stood near each other and formed the tips of a triangle. There was the "Old Synagogue," the "Small Synagogue," and the "New Synagogue" which was also known as the "New Bes Midrash"—the new House of Study.

The congregation of the Old Synagogue consisted of average "men in the street"—tailors, shoemakers, teamsters, peddlars, and also "loaders" who worked loading and unloading the freight trains, poor storekeepers and just plain beggars.

The congregation in the "Small Synagogue" was of a different kind. Here came the pious elderly men untroubled by worries about earning a livelihood, and kept sons-in-law whose minds were equally unburdened by mundane cares. Here the services began late, and before the praying began the congregants leisurely applied themselves to some religious tome.

The "New Synagogue" was the prayer house of the well-to-do. Here came the wealthy storekeepers, prosperous commission men, dealers in lumber and their agents—all men with trimmed beards, readers of *HaTzefirah*, men of "enlightened" views and with sympathies for Hasidism inherited from their fathers. On weekdays there were never more than the required *minyan* for morning prayers.

Both the Old and the Small synagogues were dim inside

23

even on the brightest days. From the ante-room one descended five steps into the synagogue itself. The Holy Ark
was built into the wall. The walls were whitewashed and
the ceilings were painted. In the Old Synagogue there was
the picture of a red setting sun right over the Holy Ark,
and its rays extended over the entire ceiling. Cradled
between the rays, and done in blue, were the tablets with
the Ten Commandments. Over the Holy Ark in the Small
Synagogue was a picture of two hands extended in priestly
benediction with the words of the benediction about them.

Both synagogues had many books in varying states of
disrepair. There were books bound in leather and in cloth,
often with missing backs. In the Old Synagogue almost the
entire north wall was lined with book shelves. In the Small
Synagogue there were so many books that all the shelves
could not hold them, and many volumes lay scattered everywhere, on the benches, on and inside the lecterns, on the
bimah.

But in the New Synagogue the books were housed in two
glass-fronted book cases. The book cases sparkled with new
varnish and the books were all in good repair. Men of evil
tongue ascribed the good state of preservation of the books
in the New Synagogue to the fact that they were never
used. Others said that the congregation of the New Synagogue consisted of people with modern ideas and attitudes,
and that they respected their books and had them rebound
whenever necessary.

The Old and the Small Synagogues were both very old.
Not even the oldest member of either congregation could
remember when they were built. "Such wood," they would
declare pointing at the woodwork, "isn't seen anywhere
these days." Leib, the bath-house attendant who was reputed to be more than one hundred years old, maintained
that the two synagogues were old even in his grandfather's
days and that "no one knew when they were built."

The new Bes Midrash was built ten years before
Shimon was born; yet, remarkably, no one knew how it

24

came to be called the New Bes Midrash instead of the New Synagogue.

This new house of worship rested on a high foundation, and it had a tin roof and rain gutters painted green. Inside, its walls were painted blue—painted, not whitewashed. The benches, the lecterns, the doors and all the woodwork was brightly varnished. The windows were big and flooded the Bes Midrash with light. The Holy Ark was not built into the wall, but stood against it and rested on a wooden base. Both Ark and base were adorned with carvings of birds, animals and flowers. Whenever Shimon went in he felt as if this were not a synagogue at all, but the private home of a rich man. He would never have been drawn there, were it not for the mystery and the shudder which he experienced looking at the unplastered and unpainted patch in the south wall which gaped like a wound in the middle of the painted area.

This patch was left barren as a reminder that blood had been shed on this wood, and that, had it not been for this blood that was spilled, the New Beth Midrash would never have risen on its foundations.

Many contradictory tales are told in town about who had initiated the plan to build the new synagogue and how the funds for this purpose had been collected. Shimon does not remember these tales distinctly. But he does remember clearly the weird story how the town artisans wanted to tear down the walls of the rising structure. When he first heard this story his imagination responded to it, and, as was his habit in such instances, he would close his eyes and reconstruct in his mind the event described with such vividness as if he had been present during its occurrence. When later he retells the story, he knows much better what had really happened than the ones who had in fact witnessed the event.

This happened on the night of *Simhas Bes haShoevah* (the festival of the drawing of water). It was quite late, but the Old Synagogue was brightly lit. All the lamps hanging

25

from the ceiling were lit, and on the hazzan's stand the candles in the Menorah were burning. The *Shir haMa'alos* had been auctioned off and for the proceeds whisky, cake and apples were bought. The adults sipped the whisky and tempered its strength with cake. The boys were given apples. Now everybody danced and sang. The best singer and dancer in the congregation was Nachum Falk Hooman, the coachman, a mighty man, tall and broad shouldered, the father of six sons who took after him. Nachum Falk did not touch the whisky. Only pale tailors and shoemakers and other chair-warmers needed liquor to make them gay, he said. He didn't require any. Why not be gay? They were in a holy place of worship, weren't they? And the *Shir haMa'alos* had been recited, hadn't they? And it was the night of *Simhas Bes haShoevah,* wasn't it? And the place was full of Jews. So what need had he of liquor? He was drunk with joy as it was. His sons, on the other hand, had managed to down a few drinks apiece.

Nachum Falk and his sons had a reputation throughout the district. It was known that where any of them had landed a blow hair would grow no more. The old man was already in his sixties and he could still pick up the heftiest peasant and twirl him above his head as one does a rooster for *kapores.* But he never raised a hand against a Jew. His sons did feel the urge to show their prowess from time to time, but they still feared their father, and he had warned them that "a Hooman is too powerful to raise a hand against a Jew."

Nachum Hooman sang and danced. He sang the verses of the hymn *Yahbienu.* ("He will hide me in the shadow of his palm, under the wings of the *Shekhinah.*") This privilege, he felt, was reserved for him every year. If anyone else dared sing it, Nachum Falk at once faced him and commanded, in Russian for some reason, "Silence!" This order was usually obeyed without further argument—Nachum Falk's voice could by itself inspire terror. But if it happened that the competitor had had a drink too many and

failed to obey, Nachum would seize him by the lapel—
actually his huge paw would clutch jacket, vest, shirt—and
lift him off the ground as one lifts a sack of straw. He
would hold the man thus and mildly urge him: "Go ahead
and sing."

The poor man thus held suspended could scarcely
breathe, let alone sing. Nachum Falk would then set him
down on the floor and remark disdainfully: "Here is a
new singer of *Yahbienu* for you! What do you think? It's
some village tune? Now listen how it should be sung!"
And he would proceed to render the hymn.

The congregation sang and danced a "circle dance" with
Nachum Falk in the center. The tails of his caftan stuck in
his crude coachman's sash, his hands behind his neck, his
mighty body seemed to float in the air; but as his feet
stamped the floor the windows rattled.

Shimon left the bench where he stood with the other
boys and joined the circle to dance opposite Nachum Falk.
(The fact that this event happened ten years before he was
born does not hinder Shimon from reconstructing it in his
fantasy.) The circle was very wide, but still it could not
accommodate everybody in the synagogue and smaller
groups of dancers formed outside it, hands on shoulders,
heads thrown back in ecstasy, feet stamping the floor.
Nachum Falk had finished his *Yahbienu,* and now the
throng was intoning the favorite tune of the Rabbi of
Chernobyl, which always had an indescribable effect on
their spirits.

In the midst of this ecstasy, Shaie the shoemaker suddenly pounded on the table on the *bimah* and shouted
tipsily: "Listen, everybody! While you dance and sing a
new synagogue is being built right under your nose. Our
well-fed big shots and their paper-reading sons-in-law are
too good to pray together with us ordinary folk. We are
good enough to work for them, to drive them to the station, but not good enough to pray with."

Motel the pottery-mender flared up in response. Motel,

27

a thin little man with a huge beard, loved all kinds of commotion, and wherever there was a dispute in town, he had to be in it. He jumped up on a bench to be better visible, and shrieked: "You are right, Shaie; you are right, as I am a Jew. Today they don't like our synagogue and tomorrow they won't like our old rabbi."

"Right!" Itche Chaikes assented. "What's to stop them from bringing a new rabbi to their new synagogue?" Itche was a man possessed by a morbid imagination. Every winter he was set upon by wolves, and during the pale nights of summer he saw devils.

"That's just what I was saying," Shaie screamed. "They will bring a new rabbi and our old, saintly, scholarly rabbi will starve to death."

"What are you babbling, shoemaker," Nachum Falk took a hand in the matter. "Who will starve? Why should our old rabbi starve?"

"You have the brain of a coachman, so you don't understand," Motel answered him.

At this point Nachum Falk's sons rushed toward Motel. "Whom are you calling names? In a minute we'll make dust out of you."

Nachum Falk restrained him. "Let him talk," he told them mildly. "What is the matter with you? You had a drink too many? What's all the excitement? I called him 'shoemaker' so he called me 'coachman.' What should we call each other? 'Rabbi'? Go on Motel, talk."

"What I mean is," Motel developed his argument, "it's clear as day. The income from the tax on kerosene will be cut in half—for two rabbis. And why only in half? Who uses the big lamps that consume pounds of kerosene? I? You? No, it's the fine folk that use them. And who brings cases for trial to the rabbi? It's they who sue each other every day. So they will bring their cases to the new rabbi, and our old rabbi will be left without a stitch of work."

"A tongue he's got—a *halef!*" Nachum Falk admired the logic.

Meantime Motel continued his harangue: "Jews! What are you waiting for? Why are you letting your saintly old rabbi starve?"

"Now you are talking nonsense," Nachum Falk lost his patience. "What new rabbi? Which new rabbi? You're talking through your hat. Get off that."

But at this point a new voice was heard from behind the *bimah*: "And have you seen the foundation? Solid stone. And the rafters! Just wait and you'll see their new synagogue will be higher than the old one."

"We won't stand for it!"

"Tear it down!"

"Pull the walls down!"

"What are we waiting for?"

The entire congregation rushed for the door, but found it barred by Nachum Falk who stood on the threshold with arms outstretched, supported on both sides by his sons.

"Nobody goes out of here," he announced, "until you, Motel, you big mouth, will answer me one question. What I want to know," he relapsed into talmudic sing-song, "is this. From what Torah will they read the weekly portion in the new synagogue?"

"What do you mean from what Torah?" Motel was in a dither. "From the same Torah that all Jews read from. There is but one Torah."

"In that case," Nachum announced, "there will be no pulling down of walls." And he turned to his sons: "If anyone dares try to go out, put his head under the faucet and wet him down; that will cool him off."

The throng realized that they were no match for Nachum and his sons, so they resorted to a stratagem. They opened the windows and began jumping out. Once outside they broke down a fence and, seizing the posts and boards, they rushed to the rising walls of the new synagogue. Nachum and his sons dashed out after them and grabbed some railings. But Nachum warned them: "There, now, my sons, no

29

violence! Bar their way and don't let them destroy a Holy Place."

But these simple people, hard-working men all year round, were now in a state of great excitement and would not listen to reason. Hampered in their destructive fury, they began wielding their wooden weapons, and the Hoomans repaid in kind. Blood flowed freely and there was no telling how the event might have turned out had not somebody brought the old rabbi to the scene. The old man was helped onto a stump and he began shouting: "Jews! What are you doing? Would you be murderers? You are shedding blood!"

His cries had a sobering effect and the crowd soon dispersed. But before they left, one section of a wall of the new synagogue was spattered with blood, and it was left thus as a reminder of the battle.

When the new synagogue was completed, Nachum Falk and his sons were invited to join its congregation. They were offered seats on the bench facing the east wall. But Nachum refused. "A man does not abandon his father's seat in a synagogue and become a 'ristocrat' just like that," he declared. Many years later his oldest son, Chaim, did buy his way into the new congregation; but by that time Chaim was well-to-do and his sons read the *HaTzefirah*.

5. *Before the Open Ark*

Four months passed since Shimon began to walk about,
but in a way his plight was now worse than before. A boy
his age should long have been going to heder. A heder boy
is occupied all day, and in his free time he has friends with
whom he can play "Kid and Wolf," "Knots," and "Mine
and Yours." On Friday afternoons in summer, the boys used
to go to the "Sands," a new suburb that had been built
near the forest and not far from the cemetery. Here were
many deep pits that for years had supplied the town with
bright yellow sand during all the years when wooden floors
were unknown, and it was the custom to scatter this fresh
sand on the clay floors every Sabbath eve. Here the boys
played a game which they named "Horseman." The game
consisted in sliding down the steep inclines into the pits
on the seat of one's pants, while holding one's feet high in
the air.

On clear summer days the boys used to go to the beech
wood near the priest's orchard. Here they could play hide-
and-seek or look for treasure buried during King Sobieski's
time. While digging for treasure, they sometimes found
human bones and then they held a funeral. It was well
known that the mounds which abounded in the neighborhood were graves of Napoleon's soldiers, and among
Napoleon's troops there had been many Jews. The bone
or the skull which they uncovered could thus have been

that of a Jew and it was a great good deed to give it a
Jewish burial.

Such were the activities of the heder boys. But Shimon
did not go to heder and wandered around idle all day. He
had no friends with whom to play. The only alternatives
were to join the girls who "baked" *halah* out of yellow
sand or bread out of dark mud, or to play at horses with
the three-year-olds. Shimon hadn't much desire for such
games, and he was also ashamed to play them.

He therefore trailed after his brother Simcha. But this
displeased Simcha because his friends didn't like to have
a baby like Shimon follow them around. It was true that
after the *Tashrak* incident the older boys tolerated his
presence, but play with him they would not—he was too
young.

The *Tashrak* incident took place a week after Shimon
had demonstrated to his brother that he knew the hymn
of praise by heart. As usual, Shimon trailed after his
brother on this Friday and, when the other boys tried to
chase him away, Simcha took his part and told them how
Shimon memorized an entire prayer after hearing it twice.
"Leave him alone," Simcha concluded. "He's no baby any
more."

But Boruch the carpenter's, who was the leader of the
gang and slow in his school work, refused to believe it.
"What kind of story are you handing us," he jeered. "I'll
bet you ten buttons he can't repeat the *Tashrak* after I
recite it twice."

"It's a bet," Simcha agreed.

The word *Tashrak* made a pleasant impression on
Shimon, though he didn't know what it meant. It was
such an uncommon word, not like the others one heard
every day. It somehow made him think of an ornate little
box. As usual when his imagination was aroused, his eyes
assumed a glassy stare. In his mind's eye he saw a little
box with a vaulted cover, like the trunk that stood in the
bedroom at home. But the trunk was big and was made of

32

ordinary wood, while this one was small and made of some special, shiny wood, and it had a bright little lock. It must contain gold and silver and diamonds belonging to Bertie the Robber. Where did he get all this treasure? It happened in this wise: It was a cold winter night and a nobleman was riding in a beautiful carriage drawn by three horses through the Yurevich forest. The nobleman had a revolver, and a Cossack holding a gun rode behind his carriage. But Bertie the Robber was not afraid of such things. He dashed out of the forest, grabbed the lead horse by the bridle and stopped the carriage.

It was strange that Shimon should think of a revolver and a Cossack, because he had never seen either of these in life and had no conception of what they were. He visualized a revolver as a kind of match that splutters when it is lit, and he thought of a Cossack as a sort of Goy, very hairy, with handlebar moustaches and wearing three swords on each side, a creature that does not talk but bellows, that does not eat but gulps, that does not drink but guzzles. Cossack and Esau meant the same thing to Shimon, and he knew what Esau was—an evil name connoting everything bad.

Boruch was about to start reciting the *Tashrak* when he noticed the strange expression on Shimon's face. He looked at Simcha, expecting an explanation.

"It's nothing," Simcha reassured him. "He's in a daze."

"Why all of a sudden?"

"Just so. He's always like that when he thinks," Simcha said and nudged his brother: "Now listen to the *Tashrak*."

Shimon was startled but pretended his mind had not wandered off. "Let him say it," he said matter-of-factly.

Boruch slowly recited: *"Tashrak, Zafa, Nimlach, Yitchaz, V'hadag, Ba."*

Shimon repeated the code word for word.

Boruch was stunned. It had taken him weeks to learn it, and here was this peanut repeating it by heart after hearing

33

it but once. His amazement gave way to anger: "You lied, Simcha; you fooled me. He knew it all the time."

"How could he know it," Simcha said, "when he doesn't even go to heder yet and doesn't know what an Aleph is."

But Boruch would not be appeased. "So what if he doesn't go to heder? You could have taught him the *Tashrak*."

Simcha swore a solemn oath: "As I am a Jew, I didn't teach him, and I never even told him there was such a thing. You don't believe me? I'll swear on a *tzitzeh*."

Boruch remained doubtful, but just then Shimon tugged at his sleeve and asked: "Boruch, what does *Tashrak* mean?"

"You don't know?"

"No," he shook his head.

"*Tashrak*, why that's the *Aleph-Bes* read backward," Boruch informed him.

"And how does the *Aleph-Bes* go?"

Now Boruch was convinced that Shimon had learned the *Tashrak* after hearing it once, but the last question again aroused his ire: "Who do you think I am? Avrom the Melamed? If you find out everything now, what will you do when you go to heder?"

From that time on the boys no longer drove him off, but they did not include him in their games. He was too small and not agile enough to share in their fun.

Therefore he wandered about by himself. Until noon it was not too bad. The synagogue was a busy place till twelve o'clock, one *minyan* succeeding another. People prayed and talked and studied. There was a constant coming and going. And wherever a group of people did something, there Shimon had to be. His ears were like sponges absorbing everything, things that he understood and others that he did not understand. But now and then he would be fascinated by the sound of a word even more than by its meaning. In general he loved to listen, and where conversation was going on, it was impossible to drive him away.

34

One afternoon in mid-Elul, when all the children had their seasonal vacation from heder, Shimon sat in the synagogue near a window. He watched the boys playing outside in the yard and at the same time kept an eye on the doings of Yude the Saint inside. He kept mental score of which boys won, and also kept count how many times Yude went to the barrel of water to wash his hands.

As he sat thus somnolent in the afternoon heat, the door of the synagogue was flung open by two women, Israel-Zalel's wife, Neche, and her grown daughter, Sarah. The two women pulled their kerchiefs down over their eyes out of reverence for the sanctity of the place and rushed toward the Holy Ark. As soon as they reached the first step, they broke out in loud laments. Shimon at once shook himself out of his stupor, alert to see what would happen.

The women wailed and their keening increased as they mounted the steps to the Ark; but Shimon noted with surprise that both of them simultaneously stopped weeping for an instant as they paused to kiss the fringe of the curtain over the Holy Ark. Then they quickly drew the curtain aside, opened the doors of the Ark and resumed their wailing. They stuck their heads inside the Ark and Neche's voice was heard presenting her complaint in traditional sing-song:

"King of heaven and earth, I have appealed to the graves, and my Zale is still sick. I have measured the cemetery and dipped the string in tallow and made candles, and my Zale is still on the verge of death. I have given his clothes to the poor, and still he is not better. I have fasted fasts and had the Psalms recited for him, and still he is in the valley of the shadow of death. So I have come before Your Holy Ark to knock on Your door. Lord of all the worlds! God! Dear Father in Heaven! Do not take away my provider, a father of eight children!"

Shimon saw Yude closing his book and hiding his face in his hands. Neche stopped to catch her breath a moment and then resumed her keening:

35

"Open the gates of Your mercy! You are called a merciful God. Show Your pity for the sake of the eight children who have not sinned."

Continuing her sobbing and sing-song lament, Neche turned to her daughter who all this time covered her face with her hands and cried softly, and addressed herself to her: "Daughter! Pray in a loud voice. Perhaps He will hearken to the voice of a bride."

Sarah began beating her head with her fists: "Father! Father! To whom are You leaving us? Who will look after us?"

Yude rose from his seat with a sigh. He still had his prayer shawl and phylacteries on. Slowly he walked up to the Holy Ark and appealed to the mourning women. "Enough, women, enough." But they did not heed him readily and Yude spoke more sternly: "Enough, women. I tell you that's enough. Go home now. Home! Don't press Him too much."

Neche closed the doors of the Ark and pulled the curtain over them. She kissed the curtain and together with her daughter descended the steps sobbing softly. They were bowed with grief and seemed resigned, now that they had taken the ultimate possible measure.

As soon as the women left, Yude looked carefully at the Holy Ark. He noticed that the curtain was not properly adjusted and went up to set it right. Then he washed his hands and went up to the book shelves. For a long time he scanned the rows of books until he selected a thin little volume and returned to his seat.

Shimon came and stopped before Yude and stared at him intently. "What do you want?" Yude asked him after a while.

"Will he get well?"

"How should I know?"

Shimon pointed to the small volume before Yude: "Doesn't this tell you?"

Yude looked at the boy's earnest little face and asked: "Are you Ben-Zion the shoemaker's boy?"

Shimon nodded assent.

"I heard about you." Yude muttered.

"Will he get well?" Shimon insisted.

Yude did not reply for a while. He rested his face on his hand and gazed into the boy's eyes. Finally he said: "Why do you think I have left my wife and children and stay in the synagogue all the time in my *tallis* and *tefillin*? Because I know nothing and understand nothing. Do you understand what I am saying to you?"

Shimon shook his head.

Yude waved his hand and muttered to himself: Why should a little boy like him understand what I mean? And to Shimon he said: "Go, go play with the boys outside. Why are you staying in the synagogue like an old man? Go play."

Shimon went out. The brilliant light struck his face. The shouting of the boys assaulted his ears. When his eyes became adjusted to the light, he looked at what they were doing. The boys were playing "Mine is Yours." Boruch had the larger army; Simcha, Shimon's brother, had but three soldiers left. Simcha called out: "Mine is yours."

Boruch: "Send your people."

Simcha: "My people are dead."

Boruch: "Come yourself."

Simcha: "Send after me."

Boruch sent one of his soldiers to capture one of Simcha's remaining men.

Shimon looked at the boys and wondered. No one seemed to care at all that Zale's wife and daughter had just appealed to God in the Holy Ark. But then why did he and Yude the Saint care?

It was getting late and time to go home.

6. *Without Boots*

Strange are the ways of memory. At first Shimon could not understand its mysterious workings. Why, for instance, should a word, or a phrase, or a verse, first come to his mind, before the desired image was evoked? Only later did he discover the close association between the seemingly irrelevant word or phrase and the particular moment of the past which he tried to recapture.

For instance, he tries to recall the morning of his first day in heder, and the word "Torah" comes to mind. This is followed by a verse from Jeremiah, and then by a stanza from a poem by Leivik. Now that Shimon knows these tricks of his memory, he closes his eyes and surrenders himself to them.

Torah. Shimon cannot recall when he first heard this word. He likes to think that it antedates conscious memory. This word is followed by the passage from Jeremiah: "Before I created you in the womb I have known you, and before you emerged from your mother's womb I have consecrated you." The couplet from Leivik crowds on the heels of the verse: "I do not know who has chosen me. . . . Anointed my youth with expectation." Shimon smiles. Now the gate to the past is open and he can recall the images at will.

When still a sitter dreamily glued to the floor with finger

inserted deep in his mouth, he knew already that books were sacred. Father's house had been poor. It contained only absolute necessities. Every piece of furniture was immediately useful: a table, chairs, a couch, a sofa, beds, and in the kitchen a work table and a rack for dishes. In the main room a large dresser, and, over the door leading into the bedroom, four built-in shelves for books. On the long wall, the one without windows, in the main room, hung a mirror. This, too, was a necessity, since the house also served as a bakery and one had to check for smudges on the face before going outside.

Like all wives of artisans, Mother did not wear a wig. On weekdays she always wore a plain kerchief on her head; on Sabbaths a silk one.

Shimon recalls that, on Fridays, Mother would stand before the mirror fixing her hair for the Sabbath, but that before removing her kerchief she would ask Simcha, the older son, to draw the curtain over the bookshelves. This was Simcha's assignment and, if he happened to be playing outside at the time, he would be called in. Simcha used to object and protested against climbing to the shelves twice, first to shut the curtain and then to open it again after Mother finished fixing her hair. Mother would chide him: "Why do you argue, Simcha? You know that I can't stand with bare head before the holy books." The argument would be renewed after she had finished, and sometimes it required a slap to add conviction to her argument. "What's the matter?" Mother would say. "Do you think we can leave the books covered? This is a Jewish home and the books must be seen."

While these disputes between Mother and Simcha raged, Shimon would follow the combatants with his eyes, suck his thumb with great concentration, and wonder how the sacred words on the pages inside the closed volumes could possibly see Mother's hair. But he learned soon that the words were so holy that they imparted some of their sanctity to the book covers. There was ready proof of this:

39

If a book fell to the ground, it was picked up and its cover was reverently kissed.

Torah! Everybody talked about Torah. Psalms were Torah. Psalms were recited all the time. There was a special society of Psalm-sayers. They were called "King David's Guards." Father was a guardsman. On Sabbaths he got up at the crack of dawn, earlier even than Mother got up on weekdays to prepare the dough. "But no matter how early I get up," Father complained, "I never get there first. There are better Guards than I."

Before Shimon could walk he knew what *Gemora* meant, and *Mishnayos*, and *Ein Yaakov*, and *Midrash*. They were all Torah. Home was filled with reverence for it, though neither Father, nor neighbor Zusie was a scholar.

Whenever Mother was angry at Father she would weep and complain: "For whose sake am I slaving my life away? Are you like Itche-Nache's by any chance? A scholar and a fine man who spends his days over a book, preparing a fine portion in the Hereafter for his wife and himself?"

At such times Shimon knew that if Father had been a scholar, Mother wouldn't have minded her labor and troubles in the least.

Gitte, the oldest sister, rocked Binyomin, the youngest brother, to sleep with a lengthy lullaby which had the refrain:

> "You will study Torah;
> You will write books."

The family couldn't boast of a single scholar or student. It was a tribe of shoemakers and tailors and carpenters and teamsters. But Shimon—he would be the scholar of the family. And Shimon's heart trembled within him at the great prospect.

Shimon now is a man already approaching old age. His hair has long ago turned gray. Were he to grow a beard, he would no doubt look like his Father at the same age. Shimon now meditates and there come to his mind disconnected words, a fragment from a biblical verse, a stanza from a poem. He knows their meaning well. "Torah, Torah, Torah. Before I created you in the womb I have known you, and before you emerged from your mother's womb I have consecrated you."

"I do not know who has chosen me.
. . . Anointed my youth with expectation."

Shimon's aging heart beats faster with excitement, as on that day long ago when, sitting on the floor, he had chosen to be a scholar and the light of the family—he, the sitter for whom everyone had only contempt. If only the day would come when he would start going to heder! Then came the Sunday morning of his first day in heder . . . but, it was a day of grief and tears.

Mornings were seldom quiet in Shimon's home. Long before the rest of the town roused itself from its sleep, Shimon's small, emaciated mother was already up. She lit the "number eight" lamp and started the fire in the oven. She waked no one before she had finished mixing a tubful of dough for beigel, and another for bread and rolls. Only then did she start rousing the family—Gitte, the oldest one, first, then Simcha, and finally Rochel-Leah. Gitte had to knead the dough for the bread; Rochel-Leah had to roll the beigel, and Simcha had to take them to market as soon as they were ready—after he said his prayers, that is.

They disliked getting out of their warm beds and tried to postpone the ordeal a while longer. This would rouse Mother's ire: Hadn't she been up for two hours already? She would shout and scold, and when this had no effect, she would resort to the rolling pin, pounding the beds with it and shouting ever louder. The house would be filled with tears, shouts, imprecations and resentment.

41

Father, who worked as a hired man in a shop till eleven at night, and had the privilege of staying in bed longer, would mutter his complaints: "This is a regular hell, a boiler factory; a man can't get a minute's rest."

His muttering only incensed Mother still more. She would dissolve in tears and a torrent of words would rush from her lips: complaints against husband, children, even God. It was a lament over her bitter fate: a houseful of eight children who refused to get up, and a husband who was always disgruntled.

Fifty years have passed since that time, and to this day Shimon can repeat Mother's litany word for word, as if he had heard it only yesterday.

The night before Shimon started to go to heder he hardly slept a wink. For months he had impatiently awaited this day when he would go to Avrom *der Langer,* the elementary teacher. For Shimon this was an occasion of mixed happiness and resentment. He was happy that he would finally go to heder; his resentment stemmed from the fact that he, a big boy, six and a half years old, would have to sit alongside children smaller than himself. By right he should have gone to the heder of Nochem the *humesh* teacher six months before.

Shimon knew that he would not be carried to heder wrapped in a *tallis*—he was too big a boy for that. They would drop no pennies on the book before him, as they did for little ones, telling them that an angel had dropped them. He was too old to believe such tales.

Shimon was filled with a great and disturbing secret. Everybody said that he had a "good head." He knew many prayers by heart, but not the *Aleph-Bes,* and in the prayer book he could recognize hardly a single letter. He knew only two, the *aleph* and the *shin,* because the first looked like a yoke with two pails at its ends and the latter resembled three poppy-pods stuck into a board. His memory retained everything he heard, but visual images he quickly forgot, unless he could associate them with something familiar.

He tossed about restlessly most of the night, and only very late did he sink into deep sleep. Usually he heard his mother get out of bed, but not this time. He finally awoke when daylight peered in through the window and he heard his mother's querulous voice:

"And you call yourself a father! A lot you care! You've known all along that the boy is looking forward to going to heder. You knew that the child needs a pair of boots. So you kept on postponing it from one day to the next, from one week to the other. And now he has no boots, and it's pouring outside, and the mud is knee-deep . . ."

Father mumbled something in reply to the general effect that his time was not his own, he was a hired hand, and that it didn't matter much in any case, so it would take another day.

But Mother would not be appeased: "Excuses, that's all I hear from you. I know you! You depended on a miracle, as you always do, 'maybe,' and 'could be,' and 'perhaps' it would turn out to be a clear day and he could go to heder in his torn shoes. But God isn't thinking of you and He does as He pleases. It's Heshvan now, and it was bound to pour. You should have known that."

"This isn't a home," Father muttered in protest. "It's hell, not home; it's a boiler factory; it's a Sambation."

But Mother would not let him have the last word and resumed her litany: "Hell, you say? Sure it's hell. A hellish fire has been burning in the oven for three hours now. Because I like it this way, because I am a witch, a shrew! I simply refuse to stay in bed like other women. I leap out of bed; I am pulled out of bed. Do you know why? Because you are a *shlemiel*; because you can't lace a shoe properly, I have to get up before dawn and stand by a heated oven. Everybody snores and I have to wrack my brain. Somebody has to do the worrying around here, like now, about the boy."

At this point Father lost his patience and burst out in anger: "Enough! The Torah will wait for him! He won't be a rabbi in any case."

Mother violently banged on the floor the rake she used to pull the beigel out of the oven. "You've made up your mind about that?" she challenged Father. "Maybe a rabbi isn't good enough for you? Maybe you want another tailor or shoemaker in the family? Of course, we are short of them, but rabbis are as plentiful as beigel in our family," she concluded sarcastically.

Normally Shimon disregarded these loud exchanges. At times he even marveled at Mother's reasoning: all her arguments sounded so convincing; each of her words had such a ring of finality about it. But this time he burst into tears. It was out of the question to go to heder in such a downpour in his torn shoes.

His crying incensed his mother still further and she turned on him: "Shut up this very minute or I will break a bone in your body. That's all I needed, that you should start crying. I haven't enough troubles without you."

"Now she's picking on the child," Father came to Shimon's assistance, but this remark only infuriated Mother so that she lost all self-control:

"Just look at him! All of a sudden he's become soft-hearted! Better go to *shul* before I throw something at you, or I do myself some violence. All of a sudden he's become a compassionate father!"

As soon as Father left the house, Mehre started to cry. She did not wipe away the tears that rolled down her cheeks. The heat from the oven dried them, and soon her face began to smart. She went into the hallway where the barrel of water stood, scooped the large copper jug full, and washed her face with the icy water. This produced a calming effect on her and for a while she stood still. Then she turned to the sofa where Shimon lay curled up, trying to be inconspicuous. She walked up to the boy and passed

44

her hand over his face. "I promise you," she said, "that you will go to heder today. I'll find some way."

Quickly she went to the oven and deftly pulled out the overdone beigel, and as she was thus engaged she chanted to the tune of the prayers in the women's prayer book:

"Well, God, I don't doubt that in the Hereafter I will catch it plenty for all this hollering and scolding. But what did You think? I would keep quiet? I will drag You to court. It's easy enough for You to sit there on Your throne of glory, surrounded by all kinds of angels and seraphim and do as You please. Of course You know what You are doing, and I don't doubt that You are right. But I have a case too. I am only a poor and weak woman, a mother of eight children, and the wife of a ne'er-do-well. But I want my children to study the Torah. I want my Sabbaths to be Sabbaths, and my holidays shouldn't be spoiled, and I have to get all this with my own two hands. So I scold. If You were in my place by this oven for one week only, You'd see for Yourself if one cannot lose one's temper and throw in a curse now and then."

Shimon listened to this monologue with bated breath. He very much wanted to know what God could answer to such perfect arguments; but he was also sure that if Mother could look at God for the least little instant she would be scared.

Mother did find a way out of the difficulty. First she sent Simcha, Shimon's older brother, to heder. Simcha had boots in good repair. Gitte went with him and they took along a pair of old shoes for him to wear in heder. When Gitte returned with Simcha's boots, Shimon put them on and Gitte led him to heder.

Shimon still remembers that the boots were far too big for him and that he had considerable trouble getting to heder in them. He remembers how his mother seated him on the sofa and pulled thick woolen stockings on his feet. His feet were then wrapped in lengths of cloth to

45

keep the boots from slipping off. He put on his brother's old coat which was still too big for him. Then Mother wrapped a big scarf around his head and passed the ends under his arms and tied them in a knot on his back. She looked him over for a moment, then she put a beigel and two rolls in the scarf. She bent over him to kiss him and said:

"Tomorrow I won't be able to kiss you any more, because you will be a Heder-Boy and you will be ashamed. Now, go, my fortune, and step off with your right foot. And remember, we have more than enough tailors and shoemakers in the family; carpenters and coachmen we also have plenty. When you grow up to be a scholar, you will take our part before the Almighty. He doesn't listen when I talk to Him in the language of a plain woman. But when you will prove to Him from the Gemora how hard it is for poor people like us to live in His world, He will have to listen to you. Now go, my child."

7. *Shimon Learns to Read*

The day Gitte took Shimon to heder the first time it was penetratingly cold and the town wallowed in mud. The downpour gave way to heavy sleet. If one stepped into the mud it was hard to pull one's feet out of it. When Gitte returned home she complained to Mother:

"A nice job you gave me, to take the child to heder to-day. The mud is knee-deep. The sleet is coming down hard. It wasn't too bad on the sidewalks; there he managed to drag his boots somehow. But crossing a street was like dragging a house. His boots got stuck in the mud, and if I pulled him too hard I was afraid he'd come out of them. I pulled him and he stands there holding on to the loops, so the boots don't slip off his feet.

"And when we got there, I was ashamed to go in. How can any one go into a decent house and track in so much mud! Luckily there was a broom in the corridor, and the water was running off the roof in streams; so I scrubbed and scrubbed and scrubbed. And when I brought him in, and took off his boots and put on him his torn shoes, I wished the ground would open up and swallow me, I was so ashamed. You know? Maybe Father was right. Shimon's scholarship could have waited another day. But with you everything must be just so."

Normally, Mother gets very angry whenever any of the children take Father's side. But this time she answered calmly:

"God will count it to you as a good deed, and reward you with a good match. You had nothing to be ashamed of. Did we, God forbid, steal anything? A day in heder is no small matter, and when Shimon grows up and becomes a scholar you will be proud that you led him to heder the first time; and it certainly won't harm your chances at a match."

When Gitte brought Shimon into the heder and started pulling off his boots, he sensed that she was upset and self-conscious, and he did not understand why. But he had no time to speculate about this. He went and sat down near the Rebbe, where a cardboard with the *Aleph Bes* pasted on it lay on the table.

The Rebbe scrutinized him and said: "Go, Shimon, go sit at the end of the table. Later I will see what you know. Meantime warm yourself by the oven. I don't know yet what to do with you."

The Rebbe was known as Avrom *der Langer*. He was a tall, lanky man with a pointed beard. Because of his height, he habitually held his head bowed. Thinking back to those days, Shimon now recalls that he resembled a ripe ear of grain.

Avrom *der Langer* turned to teaching late in life. His scholarship was very meager, but he had a good enunciation and a fine voice. He acted as cantor on weekdays, and sometimes also for the *Schachris* services on Sabbaths. He was by nature a calm and quiet person and he loved children to distraction—perhaps because he was childless himself. But he flogged his pupils just the same. Such was the custom in those days. It was known, however, that his flogging was "different." And it was told in town that, whenever a child began to cry under his punishment, Avrom's wife, too, would burst into tears and assault her husband: "Assassin! Murderer! Jew with the heart of a Tartar!" So Avrom seldom punished his pupils and chas-

48

tised them only gently. For this reason the children loved him and also benefited from his teaching.

In later years Shimon heard that it was the custom for a heder to keep an assistant to the Rebbe. But Avrom *der Langer* had no assistant. Shimon remembers his first day in heder as filled with noise and pandemonium. Every few minutes the door opened and a father brought his three or four-year-old tot wrapped in a *tallis*. With them came the mother and an assortment of aunts and uncles, and occasionally a grandparent. The child was set on the bench near the Rebbe, who pointed out to him the letters *Shin, Daled, Yud, Aleph, Mem, Tov.* The child was then coached to repeat the two words which these letters spelled: *Shadai Emeth*—God is True—and when he finally succeeded in articulating them, his father dropped a few shining coins on the *Aleph-Bes* card. The child's mother then distributed cookies, peanuts and candy to all the children, and the festive group departed to the well-wishing of Avrom's wife: "May he have a desire for learning." With father and mother gone, the child usually burst into tears. All that first morning the heder was full of the joy of the adults, the repeatedly expressed good wishes of Avrom's wife, and the crying of children.

Shimon sat by the oven as the Rebbe had told him, and observed the commotion about him. He felt a twinge of envy of the children as they were brought in by their parents, but he was not very troubled by it. He realized that he was twice as old as most of them, and that it was not for a grown boy like him to be carried to heder.

The Rebbitzin bustled about the parents and the children and appeared happy to have so many little ones about herself. She carefully distributed the goodies so that each child should get his fair share. Suddenly she noticed Shimon sitting at the oven, she looked into his wide-open eyes and at his intelligent face and wondered. What was a big boy like him doing among the tots? Shimon's mature expression troubled her. She offered him a handful of

49

cookies. Shimon took them and carefully recited the blessing over them. The Rebbitzin said Amen and moved away vaguely apprehensive. For some reason he made her think of the time she saw a pygmy when she visited Rechitse, a creature that looked like a child yet talked like an adult. She went up to the Rebbe and whispered to him: "Why did you seat him near the oven? What will you do with him?"

"Around noontime, when it quiets down a bit, I will examine him. Then I'll see what I can do," Avrom told her.

"What's there to examine him? You teach beginners. Since when does one examine beginners?"

"He is different," Avrom explained. "So don't bother me now, in all this noise. Wait till noon."

Around noontime Avrom *der Langer* called Shimon and began questioning him.

Avrom: "I heard that you know parts of the prayers by heart."

Shimon: "I know how to say 'Praise the Lord.'"

Avrom: "Let me hear you say it."

Shimon recited it slowly and distinctly.

Avrom: "What else do you know?"

Shimon: "I know *Borchu,* and *Kether,* and the *Tashrak* and grace and the blessings."

Avrom: "And do you know the *Aleph Bes?*"

Shimon: "No."

Avrom: "Why not?"

Shimon: "Nobody ever told me the *Aleph Bes.*"

Avrom: "I will say it now."

Shimon: "I have to hear it twice."

Avrom: "So I will say it twice. Now listen."

Avrom repeated the *Aleph Bes* twice, naming each letter slowly, his eyes fixed on the boy's face. Shimon stood quietly and intently watched the Rebbe's mouth. As soon as Avrom finished, Shimon repeated the *Aleph Bes* without a hitch.

Avrom pulled at his beard nervously and asked: "You're sure you didn't know it before?"

"No, Rebbe."

"Have you ever seen anything like this?" Avrom asked the Rebbitzin who had watched the procedure. "Now, I ask you, what does one do with a boy like this?"

"Say *Boruch She'omar* for him and let's see him repeat it," the Rebbitzin was eager to continue the experiment.

"Let be," Avrom said irritably. "As it is I don't know what to do, so you want to make matters still worse."

He chewed the tip of his beard and said loudly in a sing-song: "Since this is the case, and you really have such a grasp and such a memory, how long will it take you to learn to read? All by yourself, I mean?"

"I can't recognize the letters," Shimon said. "I can remember their names by heart, but I can't recognize them in the prayer book."

"Have you tried? Do you know any of them?"

"Only two, the *Aleph* and the *Shin.*"

"Why only these two?"

"Because I know that the *Aleph* looks like a yoke with two pails, and the *Shin* like three poppy pods stuck in a board."

"In that case," Avrom said, "I will tell you how to recognize the others. Listen. *Bes* is a little house with one wall missing; *Gimel* is a soldier with one leg stuck out; *Daled* is a hook with a handle on it; *Heh* is lame, see how one of its legs is not attached? *Vov* is a little stake; *Zayin* is a nail with a flat head; *Yud* is a dot with a tail. Here you have half the *Aleph Bes.* Can you remember it all?"

Shimon asked the Rebbe to repeat it, and when he did, Shimon announced: "I remember it."

"Now," Avrom resumed his sing-song, patting his beard, "you must understand that remembering is not enough. Take a prayer book and go through the pages, and on every page try and find the letters I told you about. Point them out to yourself and name them."

"You're singing, my husband. You must feel good," the Rebbitzin put in.

"Why not? Let's imagine he's an only child of ours and can do so well. It's not every day that a Rebbe gets a boy like this. Now, woman, set the table and treat him to half a glass of warm milk. He only brought with him a beigel and two dry rolls. From his home, this too is a feast."

Late in the afternoon Shimon's mother came to take him home. She brought with her the new boots which Father finished during the day. Shimon insisted on putting on the boots unaided. He went into a corner and struggled to pull them on. Meantime Mother talked to Avrom *der Langer*.

"Please, Rebbe, I beg you, don't flog the child. You must know that I never raised a finger against him. He is different from other children; he doesn't have to be beaten."

"Who said anything about flogging?" Avrom changed the subject. "But I fear that I won't be able to keep him long."

"Why not?" Mother was flustered. "Does he misbehave? Doesn't he obey?"

"God forbid, Mehre. But he is too much for me. Do you know? He learned half the *Aleph Bes*, up to the *Yud*, the first day. What's more, I only told him the letters twice and already he knows them by heart. So what will I do with him a whole season?"

"You will find something to do, Rebbe. Let him learn to read well in one season and I will be satisfied," Mehre said and began wiping her eyes with the end of her kerchief. "Perhaps God has seen my labors and my pain (Mehre often used the language of her Yiddish Bible) and is rewarding me with a scholar for all my suffering. What does a simple woman, the wife of a working man, have in life? Worries and troubles and heartache. The family is big, may no evil eye befall it, and my husband

52

is a *shlimmazel,* and we are all like harnessed oxen pulling the load. Father in Heaven! You know my lot!"

"Enough, Mehre, enough. You are sinning with this kind of talk. I think the boy has a remarkable head. But it is also possible that I am mistaken. Maybe he caught on to the *Aleph Bes* so quickly because he is almost twice as old as the other beginners. And as for flogging, don't you worry. I'm not a highwayman."

At this point the Rebbitzin intervened: "Fear not, Mehre. I'll make life miserable for him if he as much as touches the boy."

Shimon ran up to his mother, his face shining with joy. "See, Mother, how nice the boots are? Father even stitched designs on both sides of the leggings to keep the loops strong. It is a beautiful design."

Mother took Shimon by the hand, "Come, son, it's getting late, and the Rebbe has to pray *Minhah.*"

Shimon stayed an entire season with Avrom *der Langer.* The Rebbe never touched him or scolded him. Still Shimon mistrusted him. He made up his mind that the Rebbe was cheating. He was getting paid for his work yet he never examined him, never corrected his errors. The Rebbe wasn't teaching him enough, Shimon decided. He was letting him read as he wished, therefore he was being false.

Do not deceive; do your work thoroughly, do not tolerate wrongs; demand justice all the time—these were standard rules in Shimon's home. Mother always demanded justice from all—from her children, from her husband, from God. Father prided himself on his honest labor. "When I make a pair of boots," he boasted, "you can fill them with water for a day and a night and not a drop will leak out through the stitches." And when Mother finished a batch of beigel on a day when they were much in demand, she would warn her children not to be tempted. "Here, look," she would show them, breaking a beigel, "browned on the outside, and thoroughly baked within, crumbly so that it

53

melts in the mouth. A penny earned the kosher way. Not only the flour, the labor, too, is first class."

Summers especially, when Father worked on ready-to-wear jobs and earned less than usual, and the demand for Mother's baking was low, home was the scene of many quarrels. When Mother returned from market on Thursdays with baskets full of unsold rolls and beigel, and there was not enough in the house for the Sabbath, she would intone her usual refrain:

"Why am I cursed more than anyone else! Am I the only shoemaker's wife in town? All the shoemakers earn a living—a poor living but a living just the same—only my shoemaker is an exception. He works on ready-to-wear goods and insists on making boots like for kings. And so he earns enough to buy water for *kasha*. Other shoemakers put in three days on a pair of boots, but he has to take a whole week. And why? Because he has to nail the soles just so, and the loops must be stitched on to perfection, and the creases must look like an accordion. I suppose your boss appreciates you for it! You know what he says. 'If you want to make fancy boots, go right ahead, but do it on your own time; I pay for plain work,' that's what he says. So that's why you make enough for water for *kasha*."

At this stage of the argument Father would say nothing, and Mother would aim for the most vulnerable spot:

"You think you do someone a favor with your fancy work? You only help to deceive people. Your work is used as a 'come on' to lure customers."

Now Father would get angry:

"If I make a pair of boots, I have to make a pair of boots! A sole has to be nailed on, not glued on with spittle. And look who's talking, anyway! Don't you work the marrow of your bones into your dough?"

"What would you have me do?" Mother would retreat to a defensive position. "I should take money for a pound loaf and give an ounce?"

"I didn't say an ounce. But only an ounce or two less on each loaf on market day would add up to a pretty

54

penny, my saint. If I had one cent for every pound the storekeepers cheat their customers on market-day I'd be Rothschild, or at least Wissotsky."

This argument would drive Mother frantic and she would scream: "Do you hear what he says? He wants me to become a thief in my old age! Did I ask *you* to steal? All I said was you shouldn't be too big a saint. It's not your honesty I'm complaining about; it's your overdoing it which causes me and the children to suffer. Here it is the eve of Sabbath and I haven't a thing."

Stung, Father would retort: "Do I have money and refuse to give it to you?"

"You have to provide!" Mother would remain adamant. "According to the Torah, a husband has three obligations toward his wife. You are a master at only one of them. Look at the houseful of children, may no evil eye befall them. But when it comes to food and clothing, you're not there. I am entitled to them according to the *Kethubah*!"

"The notions a wicked woman can think up!" Father would be aghast. "Eighteen years after the wedding she brings up her rights under the *Kethubah*! There is no living with this woman! Have you nothing more important in mind?"

"There is no living with me!" Mother would scream. "With me . . ."

These quarrels would last till late in the night. Yet, remarkably, when Shimon now thinks back to those days, all the malice of those arguments, all the cursing and name-calling lose their sting, the coarse words and the mutual recriminations dissolve; but what remains sharply etched in his memory from this time is the unequivocal insistence on unconditional honesty, on work done wholeheartedly, on the complete inadmissibility of deceit.

For this reason Shimon was dubious about his Rebbe's behavior and suspected him of doling out false measure. Avrom *der Langer* was proud of his star pupil and showed him off before visitors. He would order him to bring a prayer book and show how fluently he could read. During the last part of the term he would tell Shimon to bring a Bible and read the *Targum*. Shimon would then fix his eyes on the text and read it fluently, while Avrom stood over him drawn up to his full height, the tip of his beard held firmly between two fingers, his body rocking to the rhythm of the boy's reading. Whenever Shimon halted at some difficult word, Avrom would freeze in the midst of his rocking, his mouth expectantly open, his eyes closed in deep concentration, and his right hand, with fingers rigidly bent, would slowly move upward. The Rebbe's entire posture then suggested great effort, as if he were trying to help the boy over the unexpected obstacle. Once Shimon mastered the word, the Rebbe's figure would relax to its former rhythmic rocking.

This was the procedure when visitors were present, but when none was about, Avrom never called on Shimon to recite. He would only tell him to open any volume at hand, show him where to begin and order him to read aloud in a sing-song. Shimon would obey, and Avrom would stare through the window while puffing on his cigarette, apparently oblivious of his charge. Shimon would become aware of Avrom's indifference and would intentionally misread a word to see if he would be corrected. But Avrom paid no attention and continued puffing at his cigarette. Shimon would then repeat the verse and read the word correctly, but in his heart was a great bitterness: The Rebbe was cheating.

During his first term in heder Shimon read the prayer book and other devotional matter many times without the Rebbe's assistance. Toward the end of the term he also read *Targum*—the Aramaic translation of the Bible. He learned to read fluently and rapidly, and to this day he can read up to one hundred pages an hour without missing the slightest nuance of phrase. When he grew up, Shimon understood that he owed this gift to the seeming negligence of Avrom *der Langer* who, by his apparent indifference to his pupil's efforts, encouraged his self-reliance and gave free rein to the boy's capacity for reading.

8. *Sholomke "Crooked Hand"*

Shimon spent only the winter term in Avrom *der Langer's* heder. After Passover he was transferred to Sholomke "Crooked Hand." Here he spent an entire year, but though he still retains a clear recollection of each day he spent in Avrom *der Langer's* heder, his memory of the time he spent in Sholomke's heder is marked by numerous gaps. Thus he can't recall the day he began studying *humesh,* or when he learned to read Rashi script. Frequently Shimon tries to recapture the recollection of these and similar events, but without success. He evokes from the depth of time other images and incidents, hoping that the sequence of events would reestablish itself. He recalls Sholomke himself, a short, solid little man with a shriveled left arm, a dense beard, small black eyes, a thin-lipped mouth drawn down at one corner to resemble a sneer. Sholomke lived on "The Sand," the quarter that was built up on the outskirts of town, near the forest. From here on into the forest extended two rows of cottages which Saichik the Storekeeper had built as summer resorts; it was rumored in town that he was making a fortune on them.

Shimon also remembers distinctly the image of Sholomke's wife, a freckle-faced woman whose kerchief always slipped off her yellow wig. She always squinted her eyes, and when she talked her squeaky voice would rise to a scream. She had a reputation in town as a sharp-tongued woman.

But Shimon remembers vividly how he was taught to write. It was a late afternoon in summer. The forest aromas drifted into the room through the open windows. Eight boys sat around the big red table; each had before him a square sheet of paper on which the Rebbe had written a form letter, and this was to be copied. But before the boys began copying the prepared text, Sholomke initiated them into the mysteries of letter writing as he paced back and forth in the room, his good hand behind his back:

"Before one begins to write anything," he chanted, "it is necessary to write down the two letters *Bes* and *Heh* separated by two apostrophes. What do these letters mean? They mean *B'esras Hashem*—with the help of God. It is customary to enclose these two letters in a small square, or a circle, as one likes. I made a square on one side of the paper, and a circle on the other.

"After these two letters, one writes down the date. This is done in Hebrew, even if one writes the letter itself in Yiddish. Thus, one does not write 'Today, Sunday,' but 'Today, the first day of the Sabbath,' or 'Today, the second day of the Sabbath.' On Tuesday one writes, 'Today, the third day of the Sabbath.' This means that it is the first, or the second, or the third day after Sabbath. On Wednesday one writes, 'Today, the fourth day of the Sabbath,' and it means that it is the Wednesday preceding the coming Sabbath. The same on Thursday. On Friday one writes, 'Today, the eve of the Holy Sabbath.' On Saturday one never writes, and if one writes a letter on Saturday night, one writes: 'At the departure of the Holy Sabbath.'

"Now write: 'Today, the fourth day of the Sabbath, the twelfth day of Tammuz, 663 according to the short reckoning.'"

He stopped for a moment, then resumed his chant:

"What the number 663 and the words 'according to the short reckoning' signify, I will tell you some other time. Now I want to explain to you the idea of the Jewish day, and what is the secret reason for writing the date in this manner and not otherwise. Pay close attention to what I will tell you. A Jew lives only for the sake of the Holy Sabbath. During the first three days of the week he lives with the memory of the Sabbath that has passed, and the other three days he yearns for the oncoming Sabbath. Now write."

The boys applied themselves to their assignment and the Rebbe stopped before the window. For a while he hummed a wordless tune, and then he resumed his chant, but this time he addressed no one in particular.

"Ai, ai, ai! Looking at those resorts, and at the rich people in them, a thought comes to mind. The Jewish day could be a very fine thing. No weekdays at all, and no worries, only a constant yearning for the Holy Sabbath. But what should a poor man do? On Sunday morning he already worries where he will get enough for the next Sabbath. He carries the Sabbath worries all the time. He would like to forget them, and to write simply, 'Today, Sunday,' thank God, six more days till Sabbath; or, 'Today, Monday,' nothing to worry about, five more days till Sabbath. And from Tuesday there is still half a week remaining. But what is one to do on Wednesday! Oh, these Wednesdays! The heart begins to tremble—tomorrow is Thursday and the wife will begin to demand: 'Give me money for the Sabbath expenses!' Thursday is a genuine hell. Where is one to take money for the Sabbath? But here it is Friday, the eve of Sabbath, and God's great miracles! the Sabbath is somehow provided for. And when Sabbath comes, it comes to all Jewish homes. Or did you think that it comes only to the homes of the rich? No. To every Jewish home come two angels and they are welcomed with the appropriate *Sholom Aleichems*."

When Sholomke started chanting this way, Shimon was ready to forgive him everything, even his avowed desire to cease being a Rebbe and become an itinerant beggar. Shimon could not believe that the Rebbe meant it in earnest—how could one want to become a beggar? It wouldn't be honest. It would be fraud.

He heard Sholomke express this idea one Thursday morning. The pupils were loudly chanting the portion of the week, and in the midst of the noise the Rebbitzin presented her appeal for money for the Sabbath.

"Sholom," she addressed the Rebbe, "it's Thursday already and I haven't a cent to my soul. What will we do about Sabbath?"

Shimon did not stop his chanting, but his ears were keen not to miss a word of the conversation. He heard Sholom answer:

"How should I know what we'll do about the Sabbath! If you wish you may depend on a last-minute miracle. I have twenty pupils, and the good God may inspire one of their fathers to send a ruble. And what if He doesn't? In that case I will have to do what I always do in such cases. Between *minhah* and *ma'ariv* I will go to one of them and stand at his door like a beggar and humbly ask whether he might not have a ruble for me. You see, it's no use to ask Isrol, the ready-made clothes man. He hasn't any. And to go to Ben-Zion the shoemaker is a waste of time. How should he have money? And to go to Isrol the teamster is a waste of effort—his horse comes before the Rebbe, because he makes a living from his horse. So again I will have to go to Reb Yakov the dry-goods man or to Reb Moishe the butcher. But on second thought, they already paid for more than half the term, so—I'll have to come to them like a beggar. What a shrew you are! You pester me when you know that I have nothing."

"I am a shrew!" the Rebbitzin screamed in rage. "He hasn't a cent, so it's my fault."

"Of course it's your fault," Sholomke answered. "If you weren't so high and mighty, Avrom-Yakov the Dayan's daughter, no less, and you'd consent that I should become an itinerant beggar, we'd have on Monday everything we need for the Sabbath. Here I have a veritable treasure.

I could get rich, if only you'd consent to it. Look at it this way: I come to some resort, like the one we have here in Kalinkovich, and I start out through the woods where the summer guests lie around like so many princes, and their women are stretched out in hammocks. All I have to do is uncover my left arm and stretch out my right arm, and dimes and quarters would start flying from all sides. And if I were to sing too!"

The Rebbitzin spat three times, "May it all descend on my enemies' heads! What the man is saying—become a beggar from door to door! For a minute I thought he meant it."

But Sholomke was not upset by her outburst and continued calmly: "Of course I am in earnest. What do you think? Teaching is not a humiliating occupation? Come to think of it, the Torah forbids taking pay for teaching, and I do get paid, so I am both a beggar and a sinner."

"Now he is laying down the law," the Rebbitzin hissed viciously. "You're only a *humesh*-teacher; leave the law to the Rabbi," she shouted and went out slamming the door behind her.

"You know what, children? It's time for you to go home to eat," the Rebbe addressed his class. "But which of you will bring some money when you come back? Or do you want me to sing you a beggar's song?"

Shimon's face flushed with shame. Why does the Rebbe talk like this! Does he really mean to become a beggar? That would be fraud. Cripples, invalids, sick people who can't earn a living go begging from door to door, but not a man who can earn his own keep. The Rebbe has a school of his own; he is considered a good teacher of *humesh*. How could he think of defrauding people! He must be joking.

But Sholomke apparently was not joking. He not only complained to his wife for not letting him become an itinerant beggar, but often, on Thursdays, when the older class was not well versed in the portion of the week, he would become angry and scold: "Goy-heads, donkeys, shriveled brains, blockheads, cattle without horns! Why do I slave with you! That's what I would like to know. I carry a treasure on my own body. I could make chunks of gold, if I were to go out cross-country begging, and here I work like a Canaanite slave and barely earn a living. I am no better than my wife if I don't spit on you and on your fathers and on my wife, the Dayan's daughter, who keeps me from becoming a beggar."

When the Rebbe scolded like this, Shimon would lower his eyes, ashamed to look at him in his self-humiliation.

One year later, when his new teacher, Mendel, taught him *Pirkei Avos* (the teachings of the Fathers), they came to a Mishnah in Chapter Four which said: "R. Shimon the son of Elazar said: Do not conciliate your friend when he is in anger, nor should you console him when his dead lies before him, and try not to see him in the hour of his disgrace." Shimon then recalled his *humesh* teacher, Sholomke "Crooked Hand." To this day Shimon cannot look at anyone who is abasing himself—he is at once reminded of his *humesh* teacher of long ago.

9. *Humesh and Rashi*

There were four *Gemora* teachers in town. Among these Reb Mendel was held in highest esteem. He was a Hasid of the Liubavicher Rabbi, a great scholar, very pious, and exceedingly effective with his pupils. He therefore never lacked students. His services were in great demand, and in consequence he was particular in his choice of them. To be accepted in Reb Mendel's heder, a boy had to be the son of a Hasid of the Liubavicher Rabbi, or his father had to be a scholar in his own right and versed in the Talmud, or the boy himself had to be both brilliant and diligent—an ornament for the heder. Reb Mendel refused to accept spoiled children over whom their mothers trembled. It was to this heder that Shimon went from Sholomke "Crooked Hand."

In town it was known that in Mendel's heder there was neither levity nor wasting of time. There one had to work hard over the Torah. Reb Mendel also had the reputation of a teacher who was not particular about his fees. He required little and had full confidence in his pupils' parents. Weren't they all Hasidim, scholars, men of piety? If they didn't send the tuition in time, it meant they hadn't any, so what purpose would be served by demanding it of them? This is how Reb Mendel reasoned.

In the intermediate days of Passover Mendel came to Mehre and asked her to send Shimon to his heder the following term. Mehre was confused for a moment. She knew that Reb Mendel was not in the habit of soliciting pupils, that usually he had to be begged to accept a pupil. Yet here he had come to her. This was an honor, to be sure. At the same time she was not too anxious to send Shimon to Reb Mendel's heder. She worried over her delicate and brilliant son, and hesitated to impose upon him the severe discipline of Reb Mendel's heder. She had planned to send Shimon to Elinke, whose heder was directly across the street, and who was known for his gentle temper. But now that Reb Mendel had taken the trouble to come to her to ask for the boy, could she shame him by refusing? Nevertheless, she offered some resistance.

"You know," she began, "that my Shimon is like an only child to me, and I know that you don't like pampered children. Besides, it is far from here to your heder, and he will have to take his lunch with him, so that the child will have to live on dry food all day. And in your heder it is necessary to work hard, and has he the strength for it, I wonder?"

"Don't look for alibis," Mendel chided her. "Sholom, the *humesh* teacher, told me that the boy is eager to learn. At home he may be a pampered child, but in heder he doesn't act like one at all. You want him to become a scholar, don't you? But Torah isn't acquired easily. Torah is a yoke. It is said: This is the way of the Torah—you shall eat bread with salt, and you shall drink water by measure, and you shall sleep on the bare floor, and live a life of need, and labor over the Torah. If you will do these, your lot will be fair in this world and good in the next one."

Mehre did not succumb to his reasoning. "Of course it is written thus, but this is meant for grownups, not for children."

Reb Mendel liked her clever reply and a smile played under his moustache. "Don't be afraid," he reassured her. "The boy will not sleep on the bare floor, nor will his

64

drinking-water be given him in measure. And I am sure that when you pack his lunch you will put in something better than bread and salt. Don't worry too much about the child. So long as he is eager to study, God's grace will not abandon him."

"And how much will the tuition be?" Mehre asked.

"The same as other *Gemora* teachers charge."

"But, Rebbe, you charge more, so I want to know exactly. My husband earns little, and I am the breadwinner here. I don't want to remain in anyone's debt, so I must have an exact reckoning."

Mendel became impatient: "You know the reckoning and you don't have to ask. I won't dun you, that you know. When you will have money you will pay. The main thing is the boy."

Mehre sighed and, as was her habit, could not refrain from complaining against a wrong. "I want nothing that belongs to you," she said, "but it's a great pity on your Neche. I can well imagine that you collect less than remains outstanding to you."

"So far she hasn't starved to death," Reb Mendel answered angrily. "And as for the children, we have to support, this we can manage. (Reb Mendel had an only son who had gone away and was never heard from again.) More is the pity on those who have children to teach and can't afford it."

He rose, quickly kissed the *mezuzah*, and went out. Mehre nodded her head and talked to herself: "His Neche is no better off with him than I am with my ne'er-do-well, but he does it for the sake of the Torah, while mine . . ." and her hand rose in a gesture of desperation, "labors to make a pair of peasant boots perfect."

Shimon liked Reb Mendel from the first day. The boy left home early, he was so impatient to see what *Gemora* was like, but the heder was a considerable distance from his home, and the way took longer than he had expected.

65

The first day he came to heder, all the other boys were already there. As soon as he entered Reb Mendel showed him his place at the table and ordered the boys to take their prayer books. Shimon stared without comprehending. Even in the more elementary school the older boys had prayed either at home or in the synagogue, yet here, in the advanced *Gemora* heder, the Rebbe told them to open their prayer books!

The boys did as they were ordered, and Reb Mendel put on his *tefillin* and wrapped himself in his *tallis*. Shimon's surprise mounted—the Rebbe was going to pray together with his pupils, instead of in the synagogue.

Shimon's surprise did not last long. The *tallis* covering his head, Reb Mendel faced the boys and said: "In my heder it is the custom that I pray together with the pupils. Today I will be the cantor. Beginning tomorrow every boy will be cantor in turn. By the end of the term each of you will know how to be a cantor.

"And now about praying. One must pray with trepidation, and fear, and love of God. Trepidation and fear, because we face a King—not an ordinary king, but the King of kings who knows our thoughts. He cannot be deceived, therefore the fear. But you must also bear in mind that the King of kings who rules over all the worlds is also our Father in Heaven, and we are His children, as it is written, 'You are sons to the Lord your God.' Therefore our hearts must be filled with a fear that does not frighten, and the longing for the Father must overpower the fear. Now let us begin."

The boys began their prayers.

To this day, almost fifty years later, Shimon clearly remembers that first morning in Reb Mendel's heder. He sat at the foot of the table, his neck craned to look into his neighbor's *siddur*, because he hadn't one of his own. The room was alive with ecstasy and enthusiasm. Every face was directed to its *siddur*, and Reb Mendel stood at

66

the cantor's desk, his arms gesticulating excitedly and his voice afire with devotion.

Reb Mendel not only prayed together with his pupils, he also studied with them. He never gave them assignments to pursue on their own, but invariably recited with each group its lesson of the day.

At one o'clock he dismissed his pupils for two hours for their lunch. Only Shimon would remain, since he lived too far away. When the boys left, Reb Mendel would remain seated, spent and exhausted, his head thrown backward, his eyes closed. Thus he would remain, as if in a swoon, until the Rebbitzin set the table. She would let him rest a long while, and only then did she cover one end of the table with a cloth and place on it half a loaf of old bread, salt, and three baked potatoes. On rare occasions there would be also some herring, half an onion, or a pickle.

When the table was set, Reb Mendel would wash his hands, recite the appropriate benedictions, and dip the hard bread into the salt. Then he would slowly peel his potato and indifferently eat his meager meal. This was followed by a glass of tea sweetened with three lumps of sugar. Finished with the tea, he would say grace and pick some volume from the book shelves. He would rock over the open book and hum a tune as he did so.

The Rebbitzin would scold: "Insatiable, that's what he is. Half the night he studied; all morning he slaved with the children; and now again a book. Better lie down and rest for the remaining half hour. Your learning won't run away; you still have the whole afternoon before you."

Reb Mendel would answer with a sigh: "Woman! Woman! You don't understand that the day is short, and the work plentiful."

Finished with this dictum he would resume his singsong, and the Rebbitzin only waved her hand despairingly: "A stubborn man is worse than an apostate. You're

67

cutting your throat with a dull knife; you are shortening your own life."

The same scene would be repeated daily without the slightest change. After a while Shimon sensed that this daily exchange contained no ill will, that it was a kind of game, their way of showing affection for each other.

Shimon learned to love his Rebbe for his earnestness and his devoted labors. "He is honest, just like Mother," he thought. He also liked how Reb Mendel never quarreled with his wife, and that he never heard from them a curse or even a word spoken in anger. Only once, on a Thursday, did he see Reb Mendel threaten his wife with clenched fists. The angry scene alarmed Shimon, but the upshot of the matter was that Reb Mendel became dearer than ever to him.

It happened in this manner. Every Thursday, Reb Mendel reviewed the week's work with his pupils. Unlike other teachers he did not content himself with merely having them recite before him, but stood behind them as they chanted, and followed them word for word in his own Talmud text, stopping at difficult passages to explain them again until the entire group knew the subject virtually by heart. He joined in their sing-song, and his voice carried above all the others. When he got out of breath, he would nod to one of the boys with a good voice to take over for a while, and no sooner did he regain his breath than he would resume his chanting. The boys energetically rocked back and forth as they chanted, and the Rebbe rocked in rhythm with them.

It was on such a Thursday, during Shimon's second term with Reb Mendel, that the Rebbe lost his temper. It was getting late, well past one o'clock, and still he did not dismiss his pupils for lunch. Obviously impatient, the Rebbitzin tried to attract his attention a number of times without success. At last she approached him and touched his arm.

"Mendel, it's almost two o'clock. Let the children go. I haven't a cent for the Sabbath."

"Don't bother me," he answered curtly.

She waited another quarter hour and repeated her plea.

"Don't interfere. We are in the middle of an important passage," he shrugged her off.

Again she waited and after a while tried once more: "Mendel, have a Jewish heart. The children are faint, and you haven't had a bite to eat. Are you observing a fast today?" And she slammed his volume of the Talmud shut.

Reb Mendel stopped in the middle of a word. His face became distorted with rage. Shimon noticed the twitching of the muscles in his neck; he saw that he tried to articulate something and could not, and then the angry words came with a rush: "Get out of here! You are interfering with the study of the Torah!"

But this time the Rebbitzin remained calm. Hands folded on her bosom she said: "Everything has its limits. It's half past two already. Dismiss the children, or their mothers will soon come to call for them. Let the children go, I say. I haven't a cent for the Sabbath; perhaps one of them will bring his fee and I won't have to go borrowing again."

Reb Mendel was flustered. He tried to say something and couldn't find the right words. Suddenly his hands clenched into fists and he rushed at her. "Get out of here before I rend you limb from limb." She turned pale and fled. Reb Mendel again opened his *Gemora*. He silently stared at the page, and closed it once more. Then he dismissed his pupils.

When the boys left, he sat down, as was his custom, with head thrown back and eyes closed. His face had a yellowish pallor. Shimon sat at the other end of the table where he usually ate, but this time he did not touch his lunch. A while later the Rebbitzin tiptoed in and silently set the table before Reb Mendel. He seemed to pay no

69

attention to the preparations. Suddenly he rose and said to Shimon: "Take the *humesh!*"

Shimon brought the *humesh* and did not know what to do with it. Reb Mendel ordered him to sit down, turned to a passage in Exodus and told him to read and to translate. Shimon began:

"And Moses went out on the second day and he beheld two Jews quarreling, and he said to the wicked one, Why will you strike your fellow?"

Pale and exhausted Reb Mendel rocked in rhythm with the boy's chant. "Now read Rashi's commentary," he commanded him. And Shimon recited: "Rashi asks: 'Doesn't it say "Why *will you* beat your fellow?" meaning that no blows had yet been struck? This teaches us that even though one has struck no blows, and has only raised his hand in anger, one is already called a wicked man.'"

Shimon stopped, suddenly out of breath. Was this what his Rebbe intended to tell him? Reb Mendel's face was white, his lips trembled and a tear rolled down his right cheek.

The boy could no longer restrain himself and burst into tears. Reb Mendel was long silent, then he said with a sigh: "Let's wash our hands."

From that day on a bond of love was forged between Shimon and Reb Mendel. It was a bond that lasted all their lives.

10. *Zalman Hooman*

From early childhood Shimon has retained a technique of dealing with people. If he does not like someone, he mentally shoves him into a dark little chamber and slams the door after him. But if he takes a fancy to a person, he takes him to the light-filled living room and seats him at the long red table facing the mirror. The first personage thus honored by Shimon in childhood was Zalman Hooman.

Mentally consigning someone to a dark chamber was the only way Shimon could inflict punishment when he was a child. Till the age of six everyone literally vented his anger on Shimon's head, for Shimon could not walk—he always sat and his head was conveniently situated for punishment. And he could not retaliate—how can one who is seated fight back? Nor could he run away. He might have reacted by derisively sticking out his tongue, but that was dangerous since it invited further punishment in the form of another slap on the head. Thus it came about that in his defenselessness Shimon invented his unique method of mental retaliation. He discovered his chamber of punishment one summer afternoon. It was a very hot day and everybody was outdoors. Mother was outside darning socks in the company of other women. Shimon sat on the floor in the corridor, thumb in mouth as usual, observing the world about him. His face had

71

that look of concentration which members of his family described as blank stare, but actually he was deeply pre-occupied. He sat at the head of the stairway which led into the garden, and there an entire new world revealed itself to him. There was the sunflower plant, tall erect, crowned with a round head. And corn stalks with thin long leaves outstretched like arms. For some reason the corn stalks reminded him of old men, and it was strange that they should have such lean arms. At the base of the corn stalks, cucumber vines twined, and pimply little cucumbers hid under the leaves. One big, yellowish cucumber lay on the ground unprotected. This was the mother cucumber. But what good was such a mother, Shimon speculated, when she couldn't help her little ones if anyone tried to pick them? Suddenly a bee flew in from somewhere and started buzzing over his head. He tried to drive it away, but it kept returning. Quickly he crawled away toward the barrel of water where it was cool and sat there a while. There he noticed the door of the store chamber. It was partly open. He moved closer and pushed the door wide open. He beheld a long windowless room. Sacks of flour lined one of the walls. A heap of rags was piled in one corner; some rods and a broken plowshare stood in another; an odd assortment of bric-a-brac filled a basin. Some big barrels, a broken chair and other discarded pieces of furniture stood against the outer wall, and high up, almost near the roof, a small square window admitted a rectangular beam of light. Shimon started to crawl into the store room but stopped abruptly when he noticed a spider swinging on a web suspended from the ceiling. His eyes followed the spider's rhythmic motion. From the darkness of the corner two yellow eyes gleamed malevolently. A cat leaped toward the light and an instant later a mouse twitched convulsively in its mouth. Shimon paled and began to retreat, his eyes glued to the swinging spider. Only when he reached the door did he dare cry out, and

72

Mother came running. She comforted him and slammed the door shut.

Ever since that afternoon Shimon had a ready punishment for his enemies. When his older brother, Simcha, hit him on the head, Shimon mentally locked him in the dark chamber together with the spider and the cat holding a squirming mouse in its mouth.

But when Shimon liked someone, he took him to the salon and seated him in the most favored spot, at the red table facing the mirror. There Mother used to stand on Saturday mornings when she put on her kerchief and prepared to go to synagogue. Shimon used to marvel how beautiful she then became, her face so calm and festive, without a wrinkle, and her eyes so mild and without a trace of the irritation of the week days. Satisfied that all was in order, Mother used to kiss him and order one of the older sisters to keep an eye on him during her absence and not to hit him. Then she would kiss the *mezuzah* and leave.

At such times Shimon felt elated. He would suck his thumb, mentally perform three somersaults, and then laugh aloud.

"What are you laughing about?" Rochel-Leah would ask.

"I just did three somersaults."

"When? How? You've been sitting there like a graven image."

"I did too make three somersaults," Shimon would insist.

"You're crazy and a liar into the bargain," his sister would counter.

"Leave the child alone," Gitte, the oldest, would usually intervene.

At such times Shimon would at once lock Rochel-Leah in the dark chamber and seat Gitte at the red table facing the mirror. But the first person to be locked in the dark

73

chamber and then taken to the living room was Zalman Hooman.

Zalman Hooman was the oldest of Nahum-Falk's six sons, and he lived one house removed from Shimon. He was a tall, broad-shouldered man with a reddish-blond beard. His eyes were light blue, his face was full, and his voice resounded like a brass bell. He was always in high spirits and his laughter was unrestrained. He loved food and strong drink and enjoyed company.

Zalman was a teamster, like his father, and owned his own team. His wagon was made of oak, and the wheels had thick iron tires. When the teamsters went out in convoy from the Kalinkovich railroad station to Mozir, Zalman was always in the lead and set the pace. In the winter, when there was deep snow, his team was in the lead to break a track for the loaded wagons. Zalman's wife, on the other hand, was as reticent as he was convivial. A tall, thin woman, she seldom uttered a word, and her face always bore an expression of anger mixed with grief. She was known in town as "The Lemon." She had no children.

Like the rest of his family, Zalman was a kindly person. "He is a diamond, a man without a gall," Mehre used to describe him. He was never seen angry, and even when he had fights with the peasants, he never lost his head. He would fight calmly. Considering his immense strength this was fortunate, for were a man of his power to lose his temper in a fight, he could easily have killed his opponent with a single blow.

Each dawn Zalman used to come Shimon's house to buy beigel. He would come early, before going to meet the morning train, and Shimon used to watch closely how he stood bent over the basket of fresh beigel selecting the crisp and browned ones. The big man's hands felt the beigel, but his eyes were fixed on Mother's every move.

Mother would stand before the oven, a small, agile woman, her face flushed from the heat, her hands incessantly restless, pulling out the beigel that were properly browned, turning over the ones in the oven, fishing out others from the boiling water to put them in the oven, and all this time issuing orders to her daughters who were helping her.

Zalman stood over the basket of beigel, the tails of his long parka tucked in his tight belt, his metal-shod boots gleaming with grease. He chewed the fresh beigel and his eyes did not leave Mother an instant. He ate many beigel without saying a word, and then he finally cracked his whip against his leggings and walked out.

Shimon's heart pounded with dread. He sensed the tension within the big, powerful man, but could not understand what he wanted. Another time Zalman spoke briefly: "Mehre," he said, "He sits above and makes messes here, below. He paired me with my lemon and you with your ne'er-do-well who is away in the villages all winter." Finished with this declaration, Zalman walked out.

But the words had their effect on Shimon. Now he knew what this tall, strong man wanted—he wanted to take away Mother—and he burst into loud wailing. Zalman returned and approached the crying child. He tenderly passed his hand over his head and face, the way he would have caressed a horse, then he remarked in his deep voice: "Why are you squealing like a pig? Five years old already, and smart too, and still crawls around like a baby."

Shimon sensed the tenderness in the rough caress and at once stopped crying. Nevertheless he mentally locked Zalman in the dark chamber for looking at Mother the way he had.

In winter, Zalman would come into the house to buy the beigel. In summer he would stand outside and get them through the open window. Shimon still recalls how Zalman stood near the window once, his face outside and his beard inside, chewing the beigel and scattering crumbs over his beard. His mouth full, he laughed and talked, and Shimon was entranced by the attractive face. The scene left a powerful impression, for to this day Shimon loves to talk with his mouth full in imitation of Zalman Hooman, and many are the scoldings he has received from his wife for this habit.

Zalman did not stand long before the window—he had to hurry to meet the train, and Shimon often cried when he left. Once Zalman returned when he heard Shimon cry and said to Mother: "He's still howling? Strangle him."

"Shame on you, Zalman. What kind of language is this? A Jew doesn't talk like this about a child."

"What do you want him for?" Zalman insisted. "You don't want to strangle him? Then give him to me. My lemon will feed him up and he will get well. What do you need him for? You have eight of them."

"Go on, Zalman, go away," Mother drove him off. "You're talking nonsense. A man has ten fingers, does he cut one of them off?"

"Then strangle him," Zalman insisted.

"If you don't go away this minute I'll scald you with hot water," Mother threatened. "To spite you, I will yet be proud of him."

Shimon knew that Zalman wasn't in earnest, that it was his way of making sport, and he liked it. So he mentally moved Zalman into the living room and seated him at the red table, facing the mirror, where Mother stood on Saturday mornings.

Shimon's attachment to Zalman dated from early childhood, and when he grew up, Zalman was proud of the boy's accomplishments and protected him.

11. *The Mark of Cain*

Days of fear and sorrow descended on the town. Near neighboring Dubnik, at the intersection of roads leading to four villages, a man had been murdered. There the body of Shaie the butcher was discovered under a heap of leaves and branches near the road. The wind blew away some of the leaves with which he had been covered and revealed the crime to a passing peasant who reported it in town.

A shudder passed through the entire town. Nearly half its Jewish population depended on frequent visits to the villages for its livelihood. What would they do now that the highways were insecure?

Shaie the butcher had gone out Sunday morning with forty rubles in his pocket to buy sheep. Usually he returned from such trips on Tuesday evening, or on Wednesday morning at the latest, leading in tow a couple of sheep. When, this time, he failed to return by Thursday, his brother took a wagon and went to the neighboring villages to inquire; but Shaie had not been seen there. The entire family was in despair that weekend. On Sunday, Shaie's body was found; his skull was smashed, the boots had been stripped from his feet, and the money was gone.

This took place in mid-Elul, and the normal mournful trepidation of this season preceding the Days of Awe was now emphasized by the murder. To add to the consternation the police did not allow the body to be buried until the prosecutor from the county seat made an investigation. Three days passed before he arrived, and then he went to the site of the murder and his police escort measured and figured and reckoned and took notes. It seemed to be an endless procedure. Then it was necessary to wait for the doctor from the city to certify the cause of death.

The victim's wife and children stormed the town. On Saturday they stopped the reading of the Torah. They besieged the rabbi's house. But the town was helpless in the face of legal procedure.

Finally the police completed their investigations and permitted the body to be buried. The entire town went to the funeral, and when Shaie's three sons recited Kaddish over the grave, there wasn't a dry eye in the entire throng. The weeping of the women and the wailing of the members of the family were heart-rending.

One week later the murderer was captured. He was a farmhand in a neighboring village. Formerly he had never had a cent to his name, and now he suddenly became a frequent visitor in the tavern and not only paid for his own drinks but also generously treated all comers. The tavern owner became suspicious and, when the farmhand paid him with a five ruble note on Sunday, he at once drew the logical conclusion and informed the village elder. The young man was questioned and his answers were contradictory. The hayloft where he slept was searched and Shaie the butcher's boots were found there, together with a blood stained ax and the remaining thirty rubles.

Four police officers brought the suspect, bound in chains, to town and took him to Avrom-Chaim's house where the local court held its sessions. The suspect was questioned again, and this time the questioning was accompanied by blows. Finally the prisoner signed the report with his cross, and then it occurred to the officer in charge that here was an opportunity to make some money. He whispered something to the policeman and went away.

Meantime nearly everyone in town had gathered around

Avrom-Chaim's house, anxious to catch a glimpse of the murderer. Shaie's brother had a heavy fence post with which, he boasted, he would break the murderer's head as soon as he was led out.

The policeman passed the word around that for a fee anyone could get even with the murderer at the rate of a quarter a blow and a ruble for sticking a pin in him. Some young men at once produced the required quarters, and a few even paid rubles. Others in the crowd raised a collection for Shaie's relatives to enable them to take revenge. Every few minutes the policeman brought the murderer to the window so that all could see him and be aroused to beat him. His blood-stained appearance at the window invariably evoked loud cheers from the crowd.

Some older men, to be sure, were much angered by these doings and scolded the crowd, but they made no impression. Avrom-Chaim himself ran around pale and frightened and begged everyone not to go in, first because it wasn't fitting for Jews to act like that, and second because such behavior might lead to Siberia in the long run. But his appeals too remained unheeded.

Shimon stood among a crowd of heder boys. They were very excited and heatedly argued where the Mark of Cain would appear on the murderer's face. One boy maintained that it would be low on the forehead, directly over the bridge of the nose; another countered that it would appear much higher, right under the hair line. Whenever the prisoner was brought to the window the partisans of the opposing points of view shouted, "Well? Who's right?"

Suddenly Reb Mendel rushed into the crowd. His pupils fled at once and only boys from other schools remained. He was pale with anger and he shouted at the top of his lungs: "What's all the jubilation all of a sudden? Satan has got hold of you. Just look at the murder on their faces. Are you Jews or aren't you?" He was supported by Avrom-Chaim and some others, and the crowd began to give way.

Shimon watched from a distance like one enchanted,

79

while Reb Mendel waved his arms, pushed and shouted: "You've lost the image of God! You're overflowing with cruelty! You're worse than the murderer. He murdered for gain, but you are willing to pay to be cruel!"

Reb Mendel noticed Shimon and addressed him: "You too are here?" Breathing heavily he took the boy by the hand and led him away. He held his hand firmly in his own hot and dry palm. At first he walked fast, and Shimon had to run to keep up with him. Then he stopped and released Shimon's hand. He took a red kerchief from his pocket and wiped his face. "You boys," he said, "argued where the Mark of Cain would appear on the murderer's face. You should have looked at each other's faces. With your cruelty you wiped the Mark of Cain from the murderer's face and transferred it to your own. It is written 'And the Lord will seek the persecuted.' Do you know what this really means? It means that the Lord begs the persecuted to permit Him to help him. Now the farmhand is no longer a murderer; now he is the persecuted."

They reached Reb Mendel's house and he invited Shimon to come in. "I have some cold *kvass*," he said. "Come in and have some, and this will give you an opportunity to recite a benediction."

Shimon sat at table with Reb Mendel and felt humbled and frightened and also proud. The house was quiet and did not seem like the same place where he sat with the other pupils every day. This was a private communion between teacher and pupil.

Reb Mendel's long fingers toyed with the half-empty glass as he spoke slowly: "You might say, of course, that the peasant boy had committed a murder and therefore merits no pity, that he deserves his punishment. This is true. So let the ones appointed to inflict punishment come and do their work; but who has set us over him to torment him?

"You are a sensible boy," Reb Mendel continued, rising from the table and pacing back and forth, "and I would

80

like you to be truly my pupil, and by this I mean not merely a boy who attends my heder, but one who follows my system. I will therefore explain to you a profound matter; I think you are capable of understanding it.

"Even one who has a legal right to inflict punishment bears within himself a trace of wickedness. Woe to the man who is by profession an executioner, an informer, or who in other ways has to enforce the law. And we, Jews, are fortunate that matters of punishment are in the hands of the Gentiles. We must shun evil even when it is decreed by law."

At this point Shimon interrupted him. "But why do you call it 'evil' if it has been decreed by law?"

Reb Mendel caressed his beard. "I warned you that this is a profound matter," he said. "If one wants to be honest with himself and right in the eyes of God, he will shun this evil. The law is for ordinary men, and abiding by it is no great accomplishment. There is higher merit in exceeding the requirements of the law. Here, look at this *midrash*."

Reb Mendel took a volume of *Midrash Rabbah* from the shelf, opened it and began reading it phrase by phrase and explaining the difficult Aramaic words to Shimon:

"Ula, the son of Kishar, was sought by the authorities who wanted to slay him. He fled to Lud and took refuge with Rabbi Yehoshua ben Levi. The king thereupon sent troops to capture him and they surrounded the city. Rabbi Yehoshua then said to Ula, 'Isn't it preferable that you be slain than that an entire community should suffer?' Ula agreed and was handed over to the troops.

"Now, Elijah the Prophet, of blessed memory, used to appear to Rabbi Yehoshua, but after the incident with Ula he came to him no more. Rabbi Yehoshua then fasted for thirty days and Elijah came to him. Rabbi Yehoshua asked him: 'Rabbi, why do you not come to me any more?' And Elijah answered him: 'Since when do I associate with an informer?' Rabbi Yehoshua said: 'Does it not say in the Mishnah: "If Goyim say to a group of Jews, 'Hand to us one of you and we will slay him, otherwise we will slay all of you,' they must all allow themselves to be slain and not hand over one man. But if the Goyim point to one man in the group, then they should hand over the man and save the lives of the others.' "

"And Elijah replied: 'Is this a Mishnah for truly pious men? Others may do so, but not you.' "

But Shimon was not persuaded. "In that case," he argued, "this is an endless matter. What would happen if everyone refused to enforce the law?"

"I know, I know," Reb Mendel waved his hand. "But who is the man who will undertake such a responsibility? Besides, we are in exile, and we do not judge in matters affecting life. Let *them* do it. I tell you, when the time comes and we are no longer in exile, should they want me to become a policeman with a sabre I will refuse. I will say, 'I do not want to; I would rather teach children.'

"I don't know whether you can understand everything I say to you, but at least you should remember that one must not rejoice over evil."

Reb Mendel sat down and again toyed with his glass. "You know, Shimon," he said in a calm voice, "I think you have great possibilities. God has blessed you with many gifts; but when one is blessed with gifts, he must also use them. You shouldn't walk about idle even between terms. It seems to me that you have reached the point where you can study by yourself without much difficulty. Tell your mother to buy you the tractate *Berakhos*. This is an easy tractate. And start studying it by yourself. If you wish, you can come to me every day around ten o'clock and we will study together. Do you agree? Now, why don't you drink your *kvass*?"

Shimon sipped the cool liquid. It was getting late, and Reb Mendel said: "Now go home. Your mother will be worried."

As he walked home, the words from Jeremiah buzzed in his head: "Before I formed thee in the belly I knew thee,

82

and before you were born I sanctified thee . . . Then I said, Ah, Lord God! Behold, I cannot speak, for I am a child."

And even as these words passed through his mind, Shimon was frightened. How did he dare apply the words of Jeremiah to himself? But Reb Mendel had said: "God has blessed you with many gifts." He tried to justify the arrogance of his spirit. He walked faster. He was eager to tell the good news to Mother, that Reb Mendel thought he could study by himself. It would make her happy.

12. *Zalman Hooman Buys a* Gemora

Early the next day Zalman came to get his beigel, as he usually did on Thursdays. Mehre asked him: "Are you going to Mozir today?"

"Am I going to Mozir? And how! They're unloading a carload of feed for Mozir today. But back we'll go empty, so I can bring you anything you want. Would you happen to need a couple of barrels of nails, for instance?"

"Never mind the nails," Mehre dampened his enthusiasm, "but I do need something for Shimon."

"And what does he need that can't be bought right here in town?"

"A *Gemora.*"

"A *Gemora* at the end of the term?" Zalman was surprised.

There was pride in her voice as Mehre told him the entire story how Reb Mendel had said that Shimon was ready to study by himself. "And the book seller," she added, "won't be in town till after Sukkos, and the boy needs the *Gemora* right away. So, here, take the money and bring him a *Gemora* from Mozir."

Zalman weighed the copper coins in his palm as he chewed his beigel. "I've carted everything in my day," he ruminated, "flour and salt and lumber and chickens and geese and dry goods and what have you—but this is the first time I'll have to run all over Mozir looking for a *Gemora.*"

"Don't talk nonsense," Mehre interrupted. "You won't have to look. Horowitz's book store is right by the river and you know it."

But Zalman would not be placated. "He's a sharp guy, that he is, and I'd rather not have any dealings with him. Some time ago I went in to buy a prayer book from him, so he says, 'That's a tough job you're taking on, brother, no easy going here.' And if I come now and ask for a *Gemora* I know what he'll say: 'You? A *Gemora*? What do you want with a *Gemora*?' And right he'd be too. Just look at me. Do I look like someone who could use a *Gemora*?"

But Mehre only shrugged her shoulders. "You don't look the shy kind to me," she said. "Since when are you afraid of a grouchy, scrawny old man?"

Zalman whacked his whip against his boot legging. "You sure got a sharp tongue, Mehre," he declared approvingly. "If I could talk like that, I'd be a governor, without getting baptized either. OK, so I'll bring you a *Gemora*, and I'll make him wrap it in the thickest wrapping paper he's got, so I shouldn't soil it with my hands." He walked away a few steps and then came back. "Mehre," he said, "you are a smart one, but this time you slipped up. You talked and talked, but you didn't tell me which *Gemora* you want."

"You're right," Mother blushed. "It's *Berakhos* I want."

All day Shimon was restless and impatient. He wandered about like a lost soul, and the hours dragged interminably. He would have liked to see his *Gemora* already, but the teamsters did not come back from Mozir till nightfall. As the sun began to set he could no longer control his impatience and started out to meet Zalman Hooman. He thought he'd go only as far as the last house on the Sand, but when he got that far and the teamsters were still not in sight, he continued walking down the road, first as far as the woods near town, and then still farther. The sun had already set, and Shimon realized how far he had gone and

85

was about to turn back, but just then he noticed a column of dust in the distance. The teamsters were coming, and Shimon stopped under a tree by the road.

As usual, Zalman was in the lead and was first to notice the boy.

"What are you doing here?" he asked in surprise.

"I came to meet you."

Zalman grinned broadly. "What's the matter, little one, couldn't wait? Wanted to see what your *Gemora* looks like? Did I guess? All right, hop right up here, alongside me."

Shimon scrambled up on the wagon. Zalman held the reins with one hand and with the other he felt in the hay in the wagon. Finally he pulled out the *Gemora* wrapped in thick paper. "Here," he handed it to Shimon. "Unwrap it. A *Gemora*—a pleasure to look at it. With a shiny leather back, and fancy binding."

Shimon's hands trembled as he carefully unwrapped the volume, and his eyes shone with delight when he saw it.

"Such a skinny *Gemora*," Zalman said. "Tell me, does it have everything that a big one has?"

"Let me look," Shimon said as he leafed through the pages. Then he nodded. It had everything that a big *Gemora* had—the commentaries of Rashi and Tosephos and Marsho. Zalman bent over to look. "Such little letters," he marveled, "and without vowel dots. Tell me now, are you sure you can make out what it says here?"

"Sure," Shimon was confident.

"So let's hear how one of our sort, a shoemaker's son, recites from the *Gemora* by himself, without the help of a Rebbe."

"Right now? On the road?" Shimon was surprised.

"And why not? What's the matter, are you ashamed of the trees? Go ahead before it gets really dark; but properly, with the right chant."

Shimon obeyed. He began slowly, and his voice was low and halting at first. But gradually he warmed to his reading, and his voice rose higher and higher. Instinctively he began to sway back and forth, oblivious of where he was.

Zalman suddenly reined in his horses and the wagon stopped with a lurch. Shimon's voice broke off in the middle of a word. The other teamsters had to stop their wagons and a commotion arose. "Hey, Zalman, what's up? What happened?"

"Come here, you whip-sticks, come over here," Zalman called to them. And they crowded around his wagon. Zalman pompously stroked his reddish beard and said to Shimon, "Start over again and show them what you can do."

Shimon was overcome with stage fright, but Zalman nudged him with his elbow, "What's the matter? Ashamed of God's Torah?" and the boy began: "When is it time to read the *Shema*? From the time when the priests go in to partake of their *Teruma*."

Their whips under their arms, the teamsters listened piously as the boy's voice floated over the treetops and re-echoed in the dusky silence. When Shimon finished the Mishnah, and began reading the Rashi commentary, Zalman cracked his whip in the air and announced: "Enough!" And turning to the others, he challenged: "Hey, you horse-skinners, whip-sticks, did you hear? Such reading! Such a voice! And now back to the horses. Whip 'em up and let's bring Mehre's pride into town in proper form, as befits the grandson of a teamster and the son of a shoemaker who starts to study on his own. All your boys can do is water the horses and take them to pasture, not read such little letters without vowel dots."

The teamsters leaped on their wagons and began whipping their horses. Twenty teams dashed forward and raised a suffocating cloud of dust. Shimon and his *Gemora* were brought into town with pomp, as one escorts a high-born bridegroom.

13. *Sabbaths*

Sabbaths were great occasions in Shimon's life. To unravel their true meaning he has to go back to his earliest childhood. In the very beginning there was a troubled curiosity about the flow of time. What happened to the day when darkness fell? And where did night go when the sun rose? Somewhat later, when Shimon became aware of individual days, he wondered about the Sabbath. Whence did it come? And what happened to the weekday atmosphere on this special day?

To the question, Whence does night come and where does it go at dawn, Shimon received an answer from Moishke *der Geller*. Looking back, Shimon realizes that Moishke was a blond young man of fair complexion. But the town did not use the term blond. Young people were classified as dark or fair, and their eyes were described as brown, black, cherry, or "cat eyes." The last designation referred to blue eyes. Blue eyes and a fair complexion were held in low esteem. Young people who were blond were disapprovingly described as *milchige*, that is, neither flesh, fish nor fowl, but of a neutral, *dairy* quality. And when, in addition, they were freckled, they were not much superior to invalids, and they were taunted that a goat would be brought to lick off their freckles. (In Yiddish freckles are called "bran.")

Moishke was a shoemaker's apprentice, and every Saturday he came to visit at Mehre's house, where the oldest daughter, Gitte, was his age. Or he may have been interested in Rochel-Leah who was already outgrowing her girlish dresses and becoming a young lady. He was a gay blade, brimful of high spirits, and reputedly knew one hundred and fifteen songs by heart. Gitte did not favor him. His complexion was so fair, like that of a peasant lad. But Mother loved him for his songs and gaiety. And Shimon was devoted to him. When Shimon closes his eyes now, decades later, he can almost sense Moishke's warm back and powerful arms. Moishke used to play a game with Shimon. Shimon would sit on his shoulders and cling to his neck with his skinny arms, while Moishke carried him from one member of the family to another and the following exchange would be repeated:

He: "Want to buy a sheep?"

She: "How much?"

He: "Three quarters."

She: "Try the others."

He: "Watch your step."

She: "I'll give you a slap."

The girl raised her hand, but Moishke would invariably dodge the raised hand, to Shimon's great delight.

Moishke loved to sing. He also could imitate to perfection the crowing of a rooster, the clucking of a hen, the neighing of a horse, the lowing of a cow. Nor were these his sole accomplishments. He could imitate various musical instruments, and when he put his fingers to his mouth and imitated a flute, Mother would be seriously worried, "You know, Moishke, perhaps you shouldn't do this on Shabbos?" But the most enchanting game was playing riddles. Moishke knew the answers to all riddles. Nearly all the riddles that Shimon later read in books of folklore he first heard from Moishke.

One Saturday when the company was thus engaged in a game of riddles, and Shimon listened spellbound, Moishke lifted him high in the air and said: "I hear you are a smart kid with a sharp tongue. So you ask me a riddle."

The girls laughed at the notion, but Mother took Shimon's part. "Goats!" she scolded her daughters. "What are you laughing about? I'm willing to wager that he will ask a riddle that will stump even Moishke."

"Well, little one," Moishke encouraged him, "ask. Let's see what you can do."

Quickly, in one breath, as if fearful that Moishke might renege on his offer, Shimon asked: "Where does the night live and where does it come from?"

Moishke swung him around and set him on the table, then he turned to the girls. "Well, since you are so smart, let's hear you answer him."

"What's the matter? You lost your tongue?" they taunted him.

Moishke scratched his head in perplexity. "This 'sitter' has me stumped. Just let me think."

He started humming a tune to the accompaniment of meaningless gibberish: "Bungo-mungo, moola-bazoola, think, now think, zippele-mippele, truly where does the night live? Bingo! I got it. Now listen carefully:

"When the sun starts to rise, the night gets scared and runs away with its entire army of shadows. The night is like a cat, like a mouse, it can squeeze in anywhere, in the narrowest corner, in the smallest hole, between the logs, in a crack in the wall, under the eaves, or under the roof shingles; but mostly it goes into chimneys. Did you ever look into a chimney? How black it is? And late in the afternoon, when the sun begins to set, the shadows start creeping out from the walls and the attics and the chimneys, and slowly night fills the entire world."

Many years later Shimon read similar descriptions of the night in the work of the Hebrew poet, I. Cohen. Carl Sandburg, too, describes the coming of a fog in similar terms.

14. *Preparations for the Sabbath*

Preparations for the Sabbath began Thursday evening. Then Mother mixed the dough for the Sabbath loaves and set it apart from the rest. Both the dough and the crib in which it was kneaded were not used for ordinary weekday purposes.

On Friday morning the usual hubbub and noise and hurry that marked the bakery work were emphasized by the impatience for the oncoming Sabbath.

Very early in the morning Shimon already had a foretaste of the Sabbath. Lying in bed he inhaled the aroma of the sugared cookies, *babka,* and *halle.* The Sabbath loaves, *halle,* were even shaped unlike the weekday loaves. They were not round but elongated and had thin, twisted strips of dough on top. They were also browned in a special way. Before being put in the oven, Mother dipped a goose feather in a mixture of oil and yolks and anointed them with this. All Jewish housewives used a similar technique, yet their Sabbath loaves never browned as glossily as Mother's did. Mother kept it as her trade secret that she added a pinch of malt and a dash of chickory—not more than a dash—to the mixture. The exact measurement was very important. The chickory had to be pinched between thumb and forefinger. A trifle more, and its taste would tell. She never revealed her secret.

When the dawn appeared blue in the windows, the special baking for the Sabbath was started. First Gitte had the monopoly on baking the Sabbath cookies; later the monopoly passed to Rochel-Leah. There were two kinds of cookies, sugared and plain. The sugared ones had to be thoroughly baked, the plain ones were only partly baked, and it required a master's touch to remove them from the oven at just the right moment so that they should not be baked through, yet be edible.

The sugared cookies were baked in two installments. First they were put on the hot floor of the oven, far from the fire, and kept there only until they formed a thin crust. They were then removed, covered with powdered sugar, and quickly, before they cooled, replaced in the oven, this time quite close to the fire. When they were finally taken out of the oven, the powdered sugar with which they had been dusted had melted and given them a brown covering that tasted like burnt honey.

The children loved the sugared cookies and never tired of them. Father and Mother preferred the unsweetened, half-baked ones. Father used to joke: "Only fools like sweetmeats, and they never know what a really delicious treat tastes like. You want to know the taste of Paradise? You want to know what manna tasted like? Then take one of the unsweetened cookies and dunk it in milk and gulp it down quick. And if there is no milk, buttermilk will do just as well."

Finished with the cookies, Mother would start on the *babka*. This she always made herself, and never allowed her daughters to have a hand in it. She used to console them:

"When you get married, God willing, you will bake your own *babka*. And if it won't come out right at first, no matter. After the wedding a husband is in love with his wife and doesn't care if the *babka* isn't just right, and by the time his love cools off you will have learned to make it right."

92

The dough for the *babka* was made with whey. The dough was rolled into a thick sheet and cut into squares, each of which was dipped in sour cream and placed in a deep pan, one on top of the other. Each layer was sprinkled with cinnamon. It was not necessary to wash one's hands before eating *babka,* as one would before eating bread, because whey instead of water was used in making the dough. The taste of *babka* is indescribable. Only one who has himself eaten it fresh from the pan, and washed it down with sweetened chickory with hot milk, will appreciate its heavenly taste.

Mother baked the Sabbath loaves last, and while she was thus employed the girls started to clean the house, to polish the candlesticks, to wash the dishes and to scour the pans. This system worked to perfection.

By the time the boys returned from heder, at noon, the house was spotless, the *cholent* was sealed in the oven, the table was set, the candles were in the candlesticks, and the compote of plums and raisins or pears was cooling on the kitchen table. An hour after noon the children's heads had been washed, the girls had changed into their Sabbath dresses, and Mother was in the living room combing her hair before the mirror. The house was filled with the aromas of freshly baked *halle,* of the Sabbath dishes, as well as with the odors of the clean clothes which smelled of soap and bluing. Shimon would feel the fresh shirt caressing his body, and his scalp would tingle from the scrubbing.

He would sit and await the Sabbath.

The Sabbath came from the Sand, near the forest, where the nice houses were. Why from that direction? Shimon could easily have explained it. On two sides the town was bordered with swamps covered with grass, low bushes and weeping willows. A variety of black berries grew on these bushes, attractive to look at, but inducing insanity in anyone who tasted them. The swamps also harbored frogs, eels, snakes, lizards and all kinds of creeping things.

Sabbath could not come from such an unclean place. On the third side of town were the railway and station. These were always noisy, full of clatter and clamor and whistling. Even on Saturdays and holidays the trains ran and the cars banged against each other. The peace of the Sabbath could not come from such a noisy quarter.

There remained the fourth side of town, the Sand, always quiet and neat, even on weekdays, and when, on Friday, the setting sun gilded the treetops in the woods on this side of town, the Sabbath made its appearance.

Where did the Sabbath drive the dullness of the week-days? To the Goyim in the village nearby, who lived in straw-thatched huts and worked in their fields and gardens even on Saturday.

When Shimon grew older he was troubled by a related question. The Messiah would come and the Jews would return to Eretz Yisrael. Where would the Sabbath drive the dullness of weekdays then? He concluded that the neighboring Gentile countries would perform the same function for Eretz Yisrael as the neighboring village did for the town. But at the end of time all the nations would become Jews, and all days would be either Sabbaths or holidays, and the dullness of weekdays would then be driven into the sea, where it would melt as salt dissolves in water—there would remain Eternal Sabbath.

But meantime not all Sabbaths were alike. Some abounded with fish and meat and soup, and even a little liquor over which to pronounce a benediction, while others were sad Sabbaths, without either fish or meat. The weekday cares that had been driven into corners for this day, peeked out of their hiding places. Mother sighed and shed a tear as she read her *Tze'ena Ur'ena*. But cares were not spoken of on Shabbos, no matter how pressing they were. Even on the most pinched Sabbaths, when the family had to content itself with dairy dishes, the table was covered with a clean and ironed cloth and the candles burned in their candlesticks. The Sabbath loaves were not

94

lacking and everyone changed to fresh clothing. Father wore a caftan and Mother a long blue skirt, and she changed her weekday kerchief to a Sabbath one. Even on the least affluent Sabbaths the meals were taken leisurely, with the entire family seated about the table. Upon returning from synagogue on Friday evening the greetings to the angels were sung, and Father recited the Kiddush with equal solemnity over the loaves instead of over a cup of wine. Normally few *zemiros* were sung at Father's table. For one thing, Father had no voice. Friday nights he was also invariably tired from his day's labors and his eyes would begin to close after the first course. On Saturdays he was tired because he would rise very early to recite Psalms. But on Sabbaths that were lacking in material cheer, *zemiros* were sung with special heartiness and enthusiasm.

One other thing Shimon remembers about those days: Father and Mother never quarreled on Saturdays.

15. *Psalms and Peasant Laments*

One Sabbath dawn and one Sabbath afternoon stand out with special clarity from among all others.

The dawn was a wintry one. In winter Father used to take the tools of his trade and a supply of leather and go from village to village to make and repair boots for the peasants. On this particular occasion he stayed away from home for six weeks. He returned one cold Friday afternoon in a peasant wagon bringing his earnings: a sack of potatoes, ten dozen eggs, peas, some hens and a brown rooster, also beets, beans, cabbage, honey, a bag of poppy seed, as well as a considerable sum in cash. As soon as he came in, Mother handed him fresh underwear and commanded: "Hurry to the bath-house before they close it. We will sort out the things you brought."

Early the next morning Shimon heard Mother waking Father: "Benche, get up."

Father sat up abruptly. "Ha? What's the matter?"

"Nothing's the matter. Time to get up for Psalms."

Through the partition Shimon heard Father mutter something indistinctly and lie down again. Mother let him sleep a few minutes more and again started to wake him: "Benche, it's getting late."

Father sat up and yawned. "You'll be the end of me, Mehre," he complained without anger.

Mother did not answer, and Shimon heard Father

puttering around with his clothes. Then, in a low voice, he began to speak in a tone of resentment tempered with good humor:

"Mehre, why do you make such a fuss about my going to recite Psalms? All the time you have arguments with God. You never see eye to eye with Him. Not long ago you complained that He sits above and meddles down here below. You wanted to change places with Him— He should have a ne'er-do-well husband and worry about a livelihood. I tell you I was scared when I heard you say such things. And now you drive me to recite Psalms. I can't figure it out."

Mother considered his argument carefully and replied with a sigh: "Don't you worry. He understood that my troubles were talking out of my mouth. What do you think? That He is just a judge like any other? He knows better and, besides, He knows what goes on in the heart. He knows that I didn't talk as I did out of too much pleasure."

Father was not very articulate and seldom won an argument, but this time he pursued the subject.

"But what good will it do you," he said, "if I earn another few *mitzvos?*"

"Benche, you're a fool," she said. "No matter how many *mitzvos* you earn, you will not be received in the hereafter with the same pomp as Leibke Sore's, for instance, because he is a scholar and he gives charity and is a *gabbai* in the synagogue. Did you think you'd be given the seat of honor in Paradise because of a few Psalms? No, you'll sit together with all the other shoemakers, near the door. And you know that a wife sits at her husband's feet in the hereafter. So where will I be? So close to the door that my feet will stick outside. So recite a few more Psalms while you can and maybe they will seat you in the first ranks of the shoemakers, so that I won't have to sit with my feet sticking outside Paradise."

Now Father became angry. "You're joking, I see," he said.

"When you ask a foolish question I have to give you a foolish answer," Mother retorted. "I always thought that man and wife are one and the same, like a door and its knob; whatever one earns, the other shares."

But in an instant she changed her tone. "Benche," she now said gently, "you never realize how good I am to you. And what if I do shout sometimes? What of it? If my wishes for you were to happen to me, I'd be satisfied. What's bad if I send you to recite Psalms? Last night you fell asleep at the table, so I woke you and told you to have another piece of chicken and another portion of *tzimmes,* because for six weeks you didn't have a hot meal. But don't forget that during these six weeks you were among Gentiles and you also didn't pray with a *minyan* even once. So now I want you to have a taste of Psalms with the Society. Is that bad? The synagogue is cozy and bright and the chant of the Psalms warms the soul. Paradise, I suppose is wonderful, but a few Psalms here, I know, are not so bad either. I only wish that we women had a *mitzvah* like this to perform."

"A tongue!" Father said admiringly. "You won't get lost in the hereafter either, with your tongue. You will give God such an argument that even He will have to concede that you're right. And then they will take you into the best salon, and I'm sure you'll drag me along with you."

Shimon heard Mother's laughter fluttering quietly in the air. "Stop it," she whispered, "it is time for your Psalms."

Father sighed: "A Mehre I got! Sweet as sugar."

This was the only time Shimon ever heard words of tenderness exchanged between his parents.

The Sabbath afternoon which Shimon vividly recalls also involved the reciting of Psalms. The Psalm-Sayers Society included nearly all the artisans in town. On Saturdays they read the Book of Psalms three times. But while their morning and noon readings were done by the members of the Society solely, the late afternoon reading was joined by practically everybody in town. Psalm 119, which consists of one hundred and seventy six verses, was generally read when the sun had already set and dusk was gathering quickly.

Shimon was present only once during the morning recitation of the Psalms, around noontime he was always in heder; but he never missed the late Saturday afternoon readings which somehow became the summit of the Sabbath because of the intensity of the mood which they evoked.

Friday afternoons the town was in haste. As the hour of lighting the Sabbath candles approached, this haste to be rid of the weekday cares assumed a feverish quality. Saturday afternoons, after the traditional nap, the town surrendered to a mood of gentle melancholy. The *Pirkei Avos* and the Sabbath *Minhah* were said in tones that lacked the cheer of the morning. When the *zemiros* were sung after the third traditional "feast" of the day, the melancholy assumed a still more somber tone. The climax of the transition from Sabbath to weekday was reached in reciting the Psalms. Yoshe the Blind led the readings by common, unvoiced consent. He was reputed to know the Psalms by heart backward as well as forward. He would stand before the lectern, his blind eyes shut, enunciating each verse with great fervor, and the audience repeated after him. Most of the audience understood barely more than one out of ten words they recited; but they put their heart's longings into the melody to which they read the Psalms, and they made it express their sorrow at the departure of the day of spiritual and physical rest, and a plea to God to lighten the burden of their harsh lives, and an appeal to come to the rescue of the people of Israel, which was like a sheep beset by wolves.

One such occasion remained forever in Shimon's memory. Yoshe was plaintively intoning: "My soul yearns for Your help; I await Your word."

Shimon did not have to repeat the words after Yoshe. They were so clearly engraved in his mind that he could almost visualize them. They were so much a part of him that he hardly thought of them as being in a specific language.

"My eyes look to Your promise; when will You console me? Though I am shrunken as a water-bag . . . I do not forget Your commandments."

Shimon had never seen a water-bag, and this single word caught his attention. He thought it must be made of the skin of an animal, and by association he remembered an old legend; When the Jews were driven into exile, they begged their tormentors to take them through the land of Ishmael. Had not Ishmael and Isaac been brothers? The Ishmaelites might have compassion on them. And the Ishmaelites did indeed meet the exiled Jews with food, but the food was salty; and when the exiles in their thirst begged for water, the Ishmaelites brought them inflated water-bags. Eagerly the thirsty exiles put the bags to their mouths; but instead of water they contained air, which entered into their guts and burst them. And that is why the prophet said, the legend concluded, "I have called on my friends and they have deceived me."

Yoshe's voice sang on: "They have almost destroyed me from the face of the earth, but I have not abandoned Thy commandments."

Shimon could stand it no longer and fled from the synagogue.

He walked past stores and houses toward the Sand and the woods that extended beyond it, not knowing where he was going, but driven onward by an overwhelming feeling of sadness. He reached Avrom Weiner's house which housed the town's government liquor store. A crowd of peasants milled in front of the house. To one side stood Anton, one of the poorest peasants in the neighborhood, and his wife Parasha, their heads leaning against each other. Anton held a bottle of vodka in his left hand, and they alternately sipped from it. Between sips they wailed a plaintive song:

> Oh my fate, my fate,
> Oh my bitter fate.
> Neither wife nor child,
> Neither cow nor field—
> Oh bitter fate of mine.

Shimon stopped to observe them as they swayed drunkenly and intoned their dirge. Then both sat down on the damp ground, Anton's right arm still around Parasha's shoulders, his left clutching the now empty bottle, and repeated their sorrowful threnody. From the distance came the tolling of the church bell.

Shimon turned and went back to the synagogue. As he came in, the *Shammes* pounded on the table to call the congregants to *Ma'ariv*.

16. *An Apple*

Shimon envied his friends who had relatives in town, because this gave them an opportunity to go visiting and be treated to goodies on holidays. Cousins also became fast friends. But he had neither grandparents nor uncles and aunts in town. His family did have some distant relatives, but they mutually shunned each other.

Shimon's mother, Mehre, was a native of Azarich; his father, Yerucham Ben-Zion, was a native of Kalinkovich, as had been his forefathers, but he had no relatives in town.

Shimon's paternal grandfather had been coachman to the Rabbi of Stalen and drove him on his travels through the towns. When the Rabbi stayed home, his coachman hauled freight between Mozir and Kalinkovich. One time —it was right after Purim—he had to bring a load of flour to Kalinkovich for Passover. The Pripet River ran between the two towns, and that year the thaw set in early. Shimon's grandfather was warned not to risk taking such a heavy load across the rapidly thinning ice on the Pripet. But he only muttered: "What? And leave a town-ful of Jews without flour for matzos?" and proceeded on his way.

He perished in the attempt and left four orphans—two sons and two daughters. The oldest son, Benjamin, was married, when still very young, to a girl from a neighboring village. He was something of a scholar and seemed to be ashamed of his younger brother, Yerucham, who became a shoemaker. Though the village where Benjamin settled was quite close, he seldom came to town, and for the High Holy Days he went to another, more distant town.

Shimon's two aunts on his father's side, married artisans in town, but both died during their first childbirths. Their husbands remarried, and dropped contact with their former in-laws. The grandmother died before Shimon was born. On his father's side Shimon had no close relatives.

Shimon's mother had brothers and sisters in her native town; her mother, too, still lived. Shimon saw them only once. The only exception was Uncle Matus, Mehre's middle brother. Uncle Matus rented orchards and made his living from working them. He would come to Kalinkovich twice each summer—once right after Tisha B'av, when he would bring two wagonloads of cherries, and the second time before Rosh Hashanah, when he would come with four wagons loaded with all kinds of fruit. It was a sight to behold. The wagons were deep and their sides consisted of closely spaced bars. The bottoms and sides were bedded with straw. The fruit was arranged in layers, each of which was covered with a quilt, and the entire load was covered with canvas stretched tightly and tied to the sides to save the fruit from becoming damaged on the way.

Uncle Matus was a tall, thin man, and dark as a Gypsy. His cheeks were smooth, without trace of hair; only the tip of his chin grew a thin, long beard that was black as soot. His eyes were a greenish-blue, like Shimon's, but much more restless.

When Uncle Matus came to town he exuded odors of fruit and freshly cut grass and a suggestion of the breezes of the fields and orchards. Lanky, mobile and gay, he used to rush into the house carrying a coattail full of fruit. He was followed by two peasants carrying baskets of fruit. It was his custom to sing out a hearty Good Morning, and follow it up at once with a description of the bounty he had brought:

"And you, Sister Mehre, look at the gooseberries I got for you, big as walnuts, and the currants are the size of gooseberries and red as fire. And the apples and plums will be brought in right away. And now you'll be busy day and night making jams; and the pears are good for Sabbath treats for the children and they are sweet as sugar and melt in the mouth; and from the plums you can make jelly, and, anyway, you know yourself what to do."

Mother usually listened to this cataract of words with a smile without interrupting Uncle Matus, and only after he had finished, she would pass judgment: "Just look at him grind away like a mill. Is this a way to come into a house? Its high time you had learned how to come into a house properly, and sit down like a father of a grown daughter, which you are, and tell about everyone in the family. And now tell me, how is Frade? And David? And Feige? And Rive? And have you heard from Shloime in Bobroisk?"

At this point Uncle Matus would outspread the fingers of his hand and start giving the count in comical fashion: "Our brother Shloime lives in Bobroisk in state and eats from a plate; David has an orchard of fruit and wears everyday a suit. Frade's boy is eight months and a day, but another is just on the way. Feige and Rive I saw with my own eyes, only day before yesterday I bade them good-byes."

Mother laughed: "You'll never grow up, Matus; you'll always be a clown, I see. But you have a kind heart, you always did. How are the kids?"

"What kids?" Mine or hers? Or all of them together?"

"Well," Mother would give up in despair, "I see I'll get nowhere with you. Better wash your hands and sit down at the table."

"Wait," Uncle Matus still hadn't finished his routine. "First come the children," and he would turn to us, who were already lined up expectantly. "For you Rochel-Leah, a plum, and you Elkele, a pear, and for myself, two plums," and he would skillfully toss the two plums into his mouth. Finished with his own treat, he would proceed: "For Simcha a pear and for Shloime an apple, and for Shimon a tweak on the cheek."

Shimon could not understand why Uncle Matus liked to pinch him. His cheeks were not especially inviting, nor was he more vivacious than the other children. He concluded that the special attention was a consequence of his superior scholarship on which the family prided itself.

Shimon wasn't especially happy over this attention which Uncle Matus paid him. To be pinched by Uncle Matus was not an unqualified pleasure. His fingers were thin and bony and hard as wire. Had he seized the whole cheek, it wouldn't have been so bad. But it was his habit to pinch a small area and to administer a twist while he pinched. This caused sharp pain and left a red spot for some time.

That particular summer, Shimon suffered a prolonged siege of toothache. Finally the ache died down and the swelling subsided sufficiently not to be noticeable; but the cheek was still extremely tender. And it was at this time that Shimon returned home from heder and found Uncle Matus seated at the table. He was cutting thin slices of bread from the loaf with his pocket knife and gingerly dipping them into the salt, then he washed them down with cold schav. Seeing Shimon, he swallowed his mouthful, wiped his mouth, and began: "Here's an apple, big as a plate; sweet as sugar, so don't you wait."

Shimon was careful not to approach too closely. He dreaded having his tender cheek seized between Uncle Matus' bony fingers. Uncle Matus observed his reluctance and pretended not to care: "You don't want it? That's all right. There will be others who'll take it with pleasure."

Now Shimon was in a quandary. The immense apple glowed on the table. Its skin glittered in the light. It was obviously plucked from the tree only a short time before, and two small leaves still clung to its stem. It was an apple to tempt anyone, yet the road to it was beset with danger. He eyed it from a safe distance. Meanwhile his brothers and sisters gathered around the table and received Uncle Matus' largesse. Seeing him occupied, Shimon edged closer to the table, hoping to escape the dreaded pinch. But as soon as he was within reach, Uncle Matus bent toward him and seized his cheek and pinched hard.

A cry of anguish so agonized that the windowpanes trembled, escaped Shimon. Even Uncle Matus was taken aback. What was so remarkable about a pinch? Wasn't this his usual greeting to Shimon? They why did he hold his face with his hands and cry so bitterly?

Uncle Matus stared at him appraisingly and announced: "Look at him, a *Gemora* boy, howling. An apple like this is worth a pinch."

Shimon whimpered: "I don't want your apple."

Uncle Matus quietly resumed his meal and declared between bites: "You are a fool, a darn fool. Just take another look at the apple. See? It's an Antonov apple, and everybody knows this kind is winey like grapes. But all regular Antonov apples are yellow. Maybe once in a lifetime it happens that there is one red Antonov in an entire orchard. And this is just such an apple. So don't be a fool. Here it is, take it. I promise I won't touch you."

Shimon stared at the apple and drooled. But he was also angry and stubborn. "I don't want your honey and I don't want your sting," he articulated between sobs.

Uncle Matus did not seem impressed with his stubbornness. "Actually," he said slowly, "I don't have to beg you at all. Whoever heard that an apple like this should go begging? But since you answered me with a quote from the *Gemora,* you have won me over and I am begging you to take it. Look at it well and change your mind."

Uncle Matus twisted the stem with two fingers. Shimon sobbed and did not answer.

"I could go for an apple like this myself," Uncle Matus concluded. "If you don't want it, that's all right." And he took his pocketknife and began peeling the apple. He peeled it slowly, making the skin come off in one long loop. The juice ran on his fingers, and the aroma of the peeled apple spread all over the house. Shimon bit his lips. He now transferred his anger from his uncle to the apple, and from the apple to himself. Why should he lose such an apple because of his stubborness?

At this point Mother came in, and her arrival re-enforced his grief and he burst into tears anew. Mother at once guessed what had happened and turned her wrath on Uncle Matus: "You and your wisecracks! You are a father of six children, and it's high time you stopped your wisecracks. Just look how the child's cheek swelled again!"

Uncle Matus waved his hand: "Never mind! By the time he is ready to marry it will heal. You always make a mountain out of a molehill, and your scholar is spoiled. So let's have no more tears. Here, you can have two hand-fuls of gooseberries and a glass of currants and two other apples, bigger ones yet. Isn't it a fair exchange? You know what? Take the whole wagon load."

But Shimon would not be consoled. His anger vanished. He only regretted his stubbornness which cost him the Antonov apple, but that was already beyond retrieve.

Uncle Matus rose. "Seems I started something. Well, it can't be helped now. Go ahead and cry. Now it's time for *Minhah*."

But Shimon's tears had one consequence. From that time on, Uncle Matus never pinched him again, not even when Shimon went to visit him in Azarich.

17. *Poverty and Charity*

Though everybody in Shimon's family who was old enough to work did so, making ends meet remained a constant worry. In winter Father went from village to village making boots for peasants and was deprived of hot meals and even of the opportunity to take a bath. In the summer he made ready-to-wear boots. There were periods of unemployment during the summer, and then Father would work as an unskilled laborer at the railway station unloading freight cars. Rochel-Leah would then bring him his hot lunch, and frequently came back in tears, announcing that she would never go there again.

"What?" Mother would rage. "You want Father to work all day on a piece of dry bread? Or do you want him to take his lunch at the counter where everything is *treif*?"

Rochel-Leah would burst into tears: "I can't bear to see him carry two-hundred-pound bales. And you should hear the language the porters use—every other word is a curse. Father works like a horse, and has to bear humiliation, and all for the sake of half a ruble a day."

This response only angered Mother. "Such a kind-hearted soul," she would say sarcastically. "She's so kind she would rather let Father go all day without a hot meal. He works hard and suffers shame, you say? And taking charity is less shameful? So far we have never taken a cent of charity and, God willing, we never will."

Rochel-Leah continued carrying pots of food to Father at the railroad station.

For all his work Father averaged not more than two to three rubles a week. Obviously it was impossible to feed ten mouths and pay tuition from such meager earnings. Mother's bakery was the anchor of rescue. She earned nearly three times as much as Father; but the entire family was harnessed to her enterprise. Even the very youngest were mobilized to string the beigel and to carry the baskets to market. And Father, too, was drawn into mother's baking operations whenever he had a free minute, to prepare kindling, or even to knead a batch of dough.

Consequently, the house always resounded to shouted arguments, recriminations and retorts. These began when Mother started waking the children early in the morning, loudly complaining about their laziness and protesting her bitter lot. She would beat a rolling pin against their beds, and when in extreme anger would also administer a blow to one or another of them. The children, in turn, protested against being roused so early; but, being helpless against Mother's demands, they vented their anger on each other. Father muttered that "seven devils" had gotten into Mother, else why should she drive everyone so, including herself. And Mother fed the fires in the oven and figuratively raked the entire family over the coals for shoving the whole burden on her, without whose efforts they would all have to resort to charity.

Excepting the Sabbaths, Shimon cannot recall a single day of his childhood that was not marred by shouts, outcries, quarrels and imprecations. Yet there was a limit that was never overstepped. For instance, in all the quarreling no obscene word was ever used, and during the most heated arguments no one, excepting the smaller children under ten, ever raised a hand against another. It was also remarkable that, though the quarrels raged with great heat, they never led to lasting anger between members of the family.

Shimon recalls one particular summer day when conditions were unusually bad. Father was unemployed and Mother's earnings dropped catastrophically. Summer was traditionally a bad season, and that day Mother didn't even bake fresh bread—there was enough left over from the previous day. When the boys returned hungry from heder that day and asked for food, there was none in the house. In their hunger they pestered her, and with unusual calm she opened the table drawer and said: "Here! See? I have nothing left except the knife."

The children were terrified. There was something about the restraint in her voice when she made this declaration that implied a challenge: "Would you have me cut myself to pieces to feed you?"

Later one of the sisters returned from market with half a basket of unsold beigel and recited her tale of woe: "What a day! The market is empty—not even a dog runs by; didn't make enough to pay for the yeast. And what will we do with the beigel? By tomorrow they'll be hard as rocks."

Finished with this portion of her lament, she waved her hand. Mother took a more cheerful view of the matter: "Maybe this too is for the good. Now the children will have something to eat. There is still some buttermilk left. With the beigel it will make a good meal. And Father hasn't had a bite to eat all day," she concluded on a minor note.

Looking back, Shimon realizes that the poverty was so great because the family shouldered the great spiritual burden of their Jewishness. Every cent over and above absolute essentials was spent for spiritual luxuries. The neighboring peasants spent such extra money as they had on intoxicants; the Jews of the town—on spiritual needs.

It never even occurred to Father and Mother to economize on tuition fees for the children. The three boys went to heder; the girls took lessons in reading, writing and prayers from a special teacher. In addition, it was an accepted rule that one must give charity. No beggar left the house empty-handed even though he may have received no more than a piece of bread or a lump of sugar. And every week Mother put at least one kopek into the *Meir-Baal-ha-Nes* donation box, and before Passover something was contributed for matzos for the poor in town. On Purim, *shalah-mones* was sent to the Rabbi, and on the eve of Yom Kippur Father left contributions in the plates specially put out at the entrance of the synagogue for donations for various communal purposes. In addition, Father was called up to the reading of the Torah several times in the course of each year, and this honor had to be acknowledged with a donation to the synagogue. Father had a permanent "seat" in the synagogue in the row facing the East wall; he had inherited it from grandfather. He never even thought of giving it up as a measure of economy.

In more recent years, when Shimon finds it hard to meet the claims of various causes, he thinks of his parents. Once he calculated his parents' donations to charitable causes, and expenses on spiritual and educational needs, and was amazed to discover that more than one fifth of their entire income was thus expended. Shimon then made it a point to keep a reminder of this fact in his check book—in case he was ever tempted to turn down an appeal.

In addition to regular charitable donations, there were also special occasional contributions. These included cases such as sudden illness in some poor family that made them need urgent aid, or the birth of a child in a poor family. There were also special "vows" made during times of unusual prosperity. Shimon remembers one such instance because he had to help Mother distribute her vowed donation. Yet mother was rewarded with humiliation by one of the recipients. It came about in this fashion.

That winter the family enjoyed unusual prosperity. Fair days were numerous and Mother's bakery goods sold ex-

111

ceptionally well. And Father, too, had an unusually good season in his travels through the villages. The entire family was provided with new clothes and shoes and, though it was still two weeks before Purim, some cash had already been saved for Passover. To add to these blessings, the cow calved a week before Purim. Now there would be no shortage of dairy foods in the house, and the calf, too, could be sold for a few rubles.

The calf was born on a very cold day and was taken indoors. The sofa was moved away from the oven wall, a quilt was spread on the ground, and the newborn creature was put there. Half-dressed, the small fry crowded about it and couldn't have their fill looking at it and admiring its qualities. Elke, who was then eight years old, couldn't get over the fact that the calf had eyes "just like a human being" and loudly broadcast this discovery. Shlomo, on the other hand, admired the hooves which were delicate and almost transparent, "just like Gitte's beads." While Breine was most taken with the restless wagging of the calf's tail.

Shimon, if the truth be told, was also anxious to take a hand in the proceedings, but was ashamed before Mother. He had his prestige to maintain—a *Gemora* boy, after all, and Mother's pride; no frivolity for him.

The noise increased and the calf became frightened. It tried to stand on its unsteady legs and could not, and this evoked still greater enthusiasm. Mother heard the noise and looked in from the kitchen. Shimon thought she would scold, as usual, but this time she smiled. She was in a good mood. "Enough gaping," she said gently. "Go get dressed. Tomorrow we will have *maladieva*."

For three days the children had *maladieva*. Then Mother wouldn't let any of them have as much as a drop of milk. All the milk the cow gave the first four days was set aside for the poor. Mother poured it into jars. By Saturday it would ferment and then she would distribute it.

That Saturday afternoon Mother called on Shimon to help her distribute the jars of milk. It was an appropriate time to do so. The third "feast" of the Sabbath usually consisted of a dairy dish; now the poor would have an opportunity to enjoy a dish of cream and sour milk.

It was a tiring job. There were ten jars to distribute, and they were not light, and then the empty jars had to be called for. The tenth jar was to be delivered to a relative who was in charge of the town's poorhouse. The poorhouse was at the other end of town. Mother would gladly have helped Shimon carry the jars, but the *eruv* which surrounded the town and according to Jewish law made it as one household, happened to be torn, and Mother therefore could carry nothing outside her own house. Since Shimon hadn't attained his Bar Mitzvah, he was still permitted to carry things on the Sabbath.

Shimon's hands were almost numb from his previous missions. The sidewalks were rough, and the streets were rutted quagmires. The contents of the jar were stirred, and the upper layer of cream became mixed with the sour milk underneath.

They approached the poorhouse when dusk set in. Shimon had never seen the inside of this institution before. The house had no hallway, and one entered directly from the muddy street into a large, neglected room. The walls, which had once been painted blue, were now a muddy gray. There must have been leaks in the roof, for large areas of damp marked the walls, which were completely bare, without mirror, picture or furniture resting against them. A long, bare table surrounded with benches stood in the middle of the room, and young men and women, dressed like itinerant street-musicians sat on the benches and sang, accompanying their song with hand-clapping. Two young men banged trays to keep time. A young woman wearing red beads and a peasant skirt danced with a young man wearing high boots. They danced with abandon, stamping hard against the floor. Mother's Sabbath kerchief seemed especially out of place in this non-Sabbatical environment.

113

Mother's relative, who was in charge of the poorhouse, greeted them: "What a guest! How come you are visiting a place like this at such a time?"

"My cow calved, Hannah," Mother said, "so I brought you a jar of fermented milk."

"And this is your scholar?" the relative asked pointing at Shimon.

"Yes."

"He looks shriveled, like a goat's turd," she said derisively.

She took the jar from Shimon's hands, removed the cloth cover and looked long into it. Her face wrinkled disapprovingly.

"Just look at it," she said with a sneer. "She brought a stirred up jar of sour milk, so no one should see that she skimmed off the cream."

"How can you say a thing like this, Hannah?" Mother protested. "How can you even think such a thing?"

"In that case, where is the cream? Or maybe a cat lapped it up?"

"It's a long way here, so the contents got stirred up."

"All right, so I believe you," Hannah conceded ungraciously. "But I know our nice housewives; they want their charity cheap, so they skim off the cream and leave the sour milk for us. They are all saints before God and man, but they want their good works at a penny apiece. And I see that you are on the way to become a nice *baleboste* too—a new kerchief on your head, and a son a scholar."

Hannah emptied the jar into a large bowl and almost threw the empty jar into Shimon's arms. "Here, scholar, take it. A good Shabbos."

Shimon reeled from the impact of the jar. Mother and son silently went out. Outside a beggar was leading a horse, apparently taking it to the watering trough. He sang out a greeting, but it was hard to decide whether there was not an undertone of mockery in it. Mehre answered him, and wiped her eyes with the corner of her kerchief.

114

"Why is Aunt Hannah angry?" Shimon asked.

Mother sighed. "It's a pity. Her Zalman earns almost nothing, and she has to take care of the poorhouse. We are first cousins, so she envies me. I have a household, and God blessed me with children. But she is like a shriveled limb."

Shimon understood. He thought of the Book of Samuel in the Bible which told how Peninah had children but Hannah did not. In the Bible the two women were married to the same man; in this case they were part of the same family—but the situation was the same.

"All the same," Mother protested gently, "she shouldn't have insulted me before so many people. She knows that I vowed to give the milk to the poor; why should she suspect me of thieving? Others may not know it, but she certainly knows that since childhood I never touched anything that did not belong to me. But if one is destined to be grieved, there is no escaping it. Still, I pity her."

At first Shimon wanted to console his mother, but he soon sensed that she did not need comforting, that she excused Hannah's rudeness, and he silently dragged his weary feet homeward.

18. *Roots*

Shimon spent three years in Reb Mendel's heder, and Mother was proud of him. She was proud that he was already able to study by himself. But her greatest joy came each Friday when he recited the weekly portion of the Bible, in the traditional chant, twice in the original and once in Aramaic, and read the Song of Songs. Neither her father nor her husband could read the weekly portion so nicely and with such fine intonation. She was also proud that Shimon was always engrossed in some book, even when he ate. She used to scold him jokingly. "If you aren't careful you'll dip your nose in the spoon. Shut the book and look at what's in the plate." But beneath the tone of reproach there was joy. When had there been such a scholar in her family?

There were none too many books in Shimon's house—only two small shelves over the door from the living room to the bedroom. Here were prayer books for everyday and holiday use, a Bible set, the Haggadah, a number of religious volumes, *Yosiffon* and the *Tze'ena Ur'ena*. The last two were entirely in Yiddish. Most of the others were in Hebrew with Yiddish translations and commentary.

At this stage Shimon seldom encountered Hebrew words or phrases that he did not understand, nevertheless he resorted to the Yiddish interpretations, especially when reading the medieval Hebrew devotional poetry which was

116

often artificially constructed for the sake of rhyme. In the Yiddish translation the rhyming was avoided, thus softening the text and making it more comprehensible and familiar. For example, he read in Hebrew the brief and rigid six-word verse describing the function of angels. He understood every one of the words. But in their Yiddish interpretation they acquired an entirely different and warm quality: "And the angels do run like lightning on the missions which God gave them, and when they have finished their work they are burned in the river Dinur, and they serve God each in his appointed moment." In this form the verse had an entirely different ring, and one could compose a long story based on it.

Even when he read the Song of Songs he retreated to the Yiddish for elucidation and justification. Shimon read: "A bundle of myrrh is my well beloved unto me; he shall lie all night betwixt my breasts." How was it possible for the Torah to contain such words? Would a modest Jewish girl talk this way? But the Yiddish resolved his perplexity, for there he read: "As the fragrance of a bundle of myrrh never ceases, so God never abandons me, He rests between the beams of the Holy Ark." Such words were more in harmony with what he heard at home and in the synagogue.

The Yiddish commentaries on the prayers also contained numerous legends. The *mahzor* for Shevuos contained all the legends about the giving of the Torah, and the Passover *Haggadah* had the parables of the *Maggid* of Dubno. Even the *Tze'ena Ur'ena* seemed more complete than the Bible. Shimon would not have admitted this in public—the *Tze'ena Ur'ena* was intended for women. But privately he read through it with the same pleasure which he derived from *Yosiffon*.

Women in town envied Mehre. "She must have special merit in heaven." Sime-Dvoire, who lived next door, hinted broadly.

Shimon recalls one Purim when Mother cried for joy

at his performance. It had been an established custom that on Purim women gathered at Shimon's house to hear the Book of Esther read to them. David the *Shammes* usually did the reading. The living room was big enough to hold all the women in the neighborhood. But that year David was sick and suggested that Shimon read the Book of Esther to the women. He was only eleven years old that year, but in case of need even hearing the *Megillah* read by a minor was considered sufficient. When Shimon finished his reading from the parchment scroll, Mother burst into tears.

Sime-Dvoire chided her: "Stop crying, Mehre; you should dance for joy, not cry. Stop crying before you incur a sin."

Mother sobbed: "I am terrified, Sime-Dvoire. All the women gaped at him as he read. I am afraid of an evil eye, may God preserve us from it."

"Against an evil eye," Sime-Dvoire said, "there is only one remedy—charity. Vow to give eighteen kopeks for charity, and no evil eye will harm him."

Mother did.

Between terms Shimon used to come to Reb Mendel each afternoon for individual instruction. This custom had been established ever since the public scene with the murderer. Not that Reb Mendel systematically taught him during these visits. The meetings usually took the form of conversations. Sometimes Reb Mendel would introduce Shimon to some passage in the Midrash, or even to the hasidic literature.

As the only hasid of the Liubavicher Rabbi, Reb Mendel felt lonely in town. He was also extremely pious, in a way that exceeded by far the ordinary piety of the town. He had no children or relatives and was himself a native of another town. His brilliant pupil, Shimon, thus became for him a substitute for friends, relatives and children, and Reb Mendel sought ways to bind him ever more closely

118

to himself. At this time it occurred to him to introduce Shimon to the *Tanna Debei Eliahu*.

In mid-Elul the itinerant bookseller came to town. He used to come twice each year—before Passover and before the Days of Awe. As usual, he arranged his stock on a table in the rear of the synagogue, and the boys gathered to gape at the array. What didn't he have there? The slightest unbound prayer book, and the overwhelming tomes of the Vilna edition of the Talmud. Ordinary Jews bought simple books accessible to their understanding; scholarly ones bought books printed in Rashi script. Reb Mendel approached the table, looked over a few volumes, then took a copy of *Tanna Debei Eliahu*.

"Reb Azriel," he said to the bookseller, "what's the price? But with reason."

"With reason, you say," Reb Azriel protested, "I will give it to you for a price that anyone would be glad to pay. But tell me, Reb Mendel, didn't you already buy one some time ago? I seem to recall that you did. What happened? It tore?

Reb Mendel leisurely caressed his *peah*. "God forbid. I guard my books, and there are no children in the house. But I want this for a gift for someone, for a pupil."

"In that case I will only charge you forty kopeks."

"That's a wealth of money," Reb Mendel said.

"Just see for yourself," the bookseller urged. "Fine paper and a strong binding, and a Yiddish version, and Rashi and *Tosephos*."

But Reb Mendel was not impressed. "You are exaggerating, Reb Azriel," he said. "The Rashi and *Tosephos* are only in the introduction, where it quotes from the *Gemora*. The other commentaries are contained in every edition. And as for the Yiddish version—what do I want with it?"

Reb Azriel was a good salesman and would not be outargued. "In that case," he said, "buy the one in Rashi script."

119

"For a boy of eleven that would be a little too hard. And, anyway, since this is to be a gift, I want it just so."

"That's just what I was saying," Reb Azriel caught him up, "for a nice gift one has to pay. So take it for thirty-five kopeks."

"I only have a Quarter."

"I can't give it to you for less than thirty."

"So where will I take the extra five kopeks?"

"I trust you, Reb Mendel. When you come for *Minhah* you will bring me the remaining five kopeks."

The copy of *Tanna Debei Eliahu* which Reb Mendel gave him nearly forty years ago still lies on Shimon's desk. Its pages are now a yellowing green, but they are intact, and when they are turned they rustle like parchment. On the fly leaf before the title page there is an inscription in flowery script, "This book belongs to the young man Shimon, son of Reb Yerucham Ben-Zion. 664 according to the short reckoning." Forty years ago Shimon packed this book with the works of Zalman Epstein, a Hebrew grammar, Peretz Smolenskin's *Wanderer in the Ways of Life,* prayer books, Dubnow's *History of the Jews* in Hebrew and a volume of Frug's poems in a box, and trundled it all the way to New York. He recalls that the travel agent, Berl Shmerels (*sic*) lifted the wooden box and said angrily: "The crazy notion of a young fellow—to haul these rags all the way to America. They will be of no use to you there." But Shimon was stubborn: "I won't leave them here." His stubbornness might not have helped him, had it not been for the intercession of Berl's daughter, Zippe. When Shimon met her fifteen years later in New York, her first question was: "Did you get those books all the way to New York?" He assured her that he did, and that he still had them.

Now Shimon turns the pages of *Tanna Debei Eliahu* and recalls the afternoon when he received the gift. Reb Mendel paced back and forth. The windows were open, and outside lay the harvested gardens. The autumn day was mild, and the coolness of the room somehow emphasized the atmosphere of gentle restfulness. Reb Mendel spoke:

"See what it says on the title page? 'This is what the Prophet Elijah taught Rabbi Anan. Happy is the man who studies this book; happy the man in whose house this book is studied, for he will attain good ways.'"

It was a moment of happiness for both teacher and pupil. Reb Mendel's words opened before Shimon a broad new world compared to which his parents' world of work and food and sleep was trivial. For Reb Mendel, Shimon was the repository of his ideas, his audience before whom he could shine. He began to read from the introduction:

"A man came to Rabbi Anan and brought him a gift of a basket of fish. Rabbi Anan asked him: Why did you bring me this gift? The man said: I had a dispute with another man and I have come to you to judge between us. Thereupon Rabbi Anan said: I am not fit to be your judge because you have brought me a gift. The man said: Then you will not judge between us, but you must accept the gift, otherwise you will deprive me of the opportunity to fulfill the commandment to make an offering of first fruits; for we have been taught that giving a gift to a scholar is the same as offering first fruit in the Temple. Rabbi Anan said: I had not intended to accept your gift, but now you have persuaded me and I accept it.

"And Rabbi Anan sent the man to Rabbi Nachman with a written note which said: Judge this man, for I am not fit to judge him. When Rabbi Nachman received the note he thought that the man must be a relative of Rabbi Anan, since he troubled to write on his account. Rabbi Nachman was then about to try the case of an orphan, but he thought to himself: Trying the case of an orphan is a positive commandment of the Torah, but it is exceeded by the commandment to honor the Torah. He thereupon postponed the case of the orphan and judged the case of the man whom Rabbi Anan sent to him. When this man's adversary saw how much Rabbi Nachman honored his adversary, he became confused, did not know how to state his case, and lost the judgment.

"The Prophet Elijah used to come to Rabbi Anan to teach him the *Seder Eliahu*. After this event, Elijah failed to appear. Rabbi Anan fasted and prayed that he should return. When Elijah finally came, Rabbi Anan was afraid to look at him, and he sat in an adjoining room. Elijah finished teaching Rabbi Anan the entire *Seder Eliahu*. This is why this book is divided into *Seder Eliahu Rabba*, and *Seder Eliahu Zutta*. The part which Elijah taught Rabbi Anan face to face is called *Rabba*, the Great, and the part which he taught him when they were in separate rooms is called *Zutta*, the Small."

Reb Mendel paused a moment, then went on.

"In this tale, which is taken from the *Gemora*, Tractate Kesubos, lies a profound meaning and it teaches us a great lesson. A scholar must be extremely careful in whatever he does, otherwise he is not a true scholar. A Jew who is a scholar must not eat while standing up, nor lick his fingers, nor belch in the presence of people. He must be temperate in his food and drink, and careful of his garb, and he must not raise his voice. A scholar whose garment is spotted deserves death at the hands of Heaven, because he has aroused the disrespect of people for the Torah."

Reb Mendel talked a long time and Shimon allowed his words to penetrate deeply into himself. Reb Mendel talked of the duties of a scholar. He must have meant Shimon, the boy concluded. He, Shimon, the son of a shoemaker, was held fit to wear the crown of *learning*. He lacked high birth, and his family had no wealth, but the temple of learning was open to him and he could enter it and make it his home, by his own efforts without assistance. Scholarship depended on himself alone, he jubilated.

Later he went home, the volume held tightly under his arm. The town was peaceful in the autumn afternoon,

and it seemed to Shimon that it had been there since the
beginning of time and that no storm could upset it. In
this Jewish realm which was the town, the scholars were
the greatest aristocrats, and now they opened the doors
of their palaces before him.

That season between terms was a happy one for Shimon.
Reb Mendel became closer to him than his parents. Every
afternoon they studied together, and quickly went through
the entire *Tanna Debei Eliahu.* When Shimon now leafs
through the volume, he frequently turns to Chapter Fourteen. Strong memories are associated with it. Reb Mendel
read and interpreted it for him. He read:

"Two things in the world I love from the depth of my
heart, the Torah and the people of Israel. But I do not
know which comes first. So I said to him: In the world it
is said that Torah comes first, but I say that Israel comes
first, for were it not for the Jews the world would not
have been created; and had it been created, it would have
been destroyed."

"Do you understand, Shimon, the meaning of this?"
Reb Mendel asked. "Who is it that says, 'But I say that
Israel comes first'? It is the prophet Elijah who said it,
the same Prophet Elijah who wanders through all Jewish
towns and villages, who is present at every *b'rith* and
seder. He knows Israel and its greatness and holiness. He
knows how Jews live and suffer and still remain Jews.
That is why his love of Israel is so great, and in him the
measure of compassion always triumphs over the measure
of law."

Reb Mendel was carried away and continued: "All the
words of chastisement which the prophets addressed to the
Jews were uttered because Israel is precious in the eyes
of God. Had the Jews been like other nations, the prophets
would not have troubled about them."

Recalling Reb Mendel's peroration, Shimon smiles. Only
recently a Yiddish writer argued with him and said: "The
trouble with you, Shimon, is that you are too much ad-

123

dicted to love of Israel. Even when you speak critically of Jews you lift them out of the context of other peoples. But Jews are like all other people, neither better nor worse—though sometimes it seems to me that they are worse."

Shimon thought as he listened to him. "Evidently he never had a Rebbe like Reb Mendel. Otherwise he could not detach himself so thoroughly from his roots."

Shimon's roots go back to Reb Mendel, the *Tanna Debei Eliahu,* and still farther back.

19. *The Old Tailor*

At midnight a low heart-rending lament awakened Shimon from his sleep. He sat up abruptly in his bed. Soon the words became distinct. Someone was intoning:

"How long, Oh Lord, will Thy congregation mourn bitterly
 For Thy house of prayer burned by the foe;
 Oh, God, the heathens came into Thine inheritance."

Now Shimon realized what it was. Someone was observing the midnight mourning for the destroyed Temple. But who could it be? Certainly not Father. Few in the entire street were so pious as to practice the midnight mourning, and one of them was Leibke Sore's, who lived next door. A tall, thin man, emaciated by many fasts, he was devoted to praying and was always the last the leave the synagogue. Almost invariably he swayed over some open volume. On summer nights, when the windows were open, Shimon often heard him intoning the midnight laments. But now the mournful melody came from within the house. Shimon held his breath, trying to recognize the voice. It was a stranger's voice. Who could it be?

Goaded by curiosity Shimon stealthily left his bed and approached the door. On an overturned bench near the sofa sat a small, shriveled old man. His hair was completely white. A thick prayer book lay on a tabouret nearby and a burning candle shed a circle of gloom about him. His head rested on the palm of his right hand. His forehead was covered with ashes. Tears streamed down his face as he intoned his litany. He pronounced the words distinctly, but not loudly, so as not to awaken the household.

Shimon recognized the man and returned to his bed. This was his granduncle, Reb Ore. For thirty years he had been a rabbi, then he suddenly abandoned the rabbinate and became a tailor, like his father. At the time this created quite a stir in the entire district, and various stories circulated regarding the reason for his strange move. In town it was said that he left the rabbinate because his father had been insulted at a public meeting.

It was told that in the community where he had served as rabbi, a quarrel had broken out between some important personages. After some time the two contending sides agreed to arbitrate their dispute before a court of three rabbis. Two rabbis were brought from neighboring towns and Reb Ore served as the third arbitrator. The case was weighed a long time, and finally a judgment was rendered. Reb Ore delivered the decision. The man who lost the case was not only rich, but also a great scholar and prominent socially. He felt that an injustice had been done him. Besides, he somehow learned that the other two rabbis at first wished to decide in his favor, but Reb Ore persuaded them to the contrary. He submitted to the judgment, but in his injured pride he was determined to insult Reb Ore, who was the son of a tailor.

One day he approached Reb Ore and engaged him in scholarly conversation. "You know, Rabbi," he began, "there is a verse in the Torah which always troubled me. It is written that God said to the generation of desert wanderers: 'Thy raiment waxed not old upon thee, neither did thy foot swell, these forty years.' I never could understand the connection between the two. Swollen feet are an ailment, a misfortune, and when the generation of the exodus from Egypt walked in the desert for forty years

126

and their feet did not swell it was indeed a blessing. But what advantage was there in their wearing the same garments for forty years? But now I have found the answer to this question: it is equally a misfortune to live under the rule of tailors."

The other rabbis, who were present when this insult was inflicted, did not scold the man; in fact, they even smiled at the sharpness of the barb. Then Reb Ore said: "Since my being a rabbi shames my father, I will no longer be one." All appeals that he should reverse his decision were fruitless. He abandoned the rabbinate and returned to his native town, Paritch, where he engaged in his father's occupation—tailoring.

Shimon had heard much about this granduncle, but he had only seen him once before. Now the old man was in the house. When did he come to town? Who had let him in?

The plaintive melody penetrated into Shimon's room.

"Woe, God's tent is torn down,
   The world is destroyed;
   The light of the stars is dimmed,
   The High Priest is no more in the Temple."

Shimon strained to go on listening, but sleep gradually overcame him.

Early in the morning he was awakened by Mother's scolding. She seemed to be angry at somebody and she talked loudly. Her arguments were directed against Uncle Ore. Though he was not present, she addressed him as if he were standing nearby.

Half asleep, Shimon at first could not follow the drift of her talk. She talked very fast, and the remarks she addressed to Uncle Ore were interspersed with orders and instructions to Rochel-Leah who was rolling the beigel, to Shlomo who was preparing to go to market. Finally Shimon disentangled the thread of her argument:

"I won't be ashamed to say it to his face; just as soon

127

as he comes back from the synagogue I'll ask him. Such a wrong must not be passed over in silence."

Shimon wondered: What kind of great wrong could Reb Ore have committed that Mother didn't want to be silent about it?

Shimon dressed, washed his hands, and started to work. His job early in the morning consisted in stringing the beigel, ten to a batch. He often wondered at the strange way things were done. The beigel were sold ten for five kopeks, but on every sale two extra beigel were thrown in for good measure. So why not string them by the dozen to begin with? But this morning his mind was not free for these speculations. He wanted to know what it was his granduncle was guilty of.

Reb Ore returned from the synagogue and Mother set the table for him. He washed and piously recited *Se'u Yedekhem,* then he raised his hands, shut his eyes and pronounced the benediction with great concentration. Slowly he dipped the bread in the salt and began to eat. Mother faced him, arms akimbo. For a while she was silent, as if wondering how to begin; but when she started to talk, her words came in a rush.

"You tell me, Reb Ore, explain it to me. You are a rabbi, a scholar, may my Shimon be no less. People say you are a saint, and when you no longer wanted to be a rabbi, the entire district talked about it. It's no small matter to abandon the rabbinate and become a tailor. I don't grasp it. Aren't there enough tailors in the family? But I am a woman, and it's not a woman's business to meddle in such matters. But now, Reb Ore, I am not talking about the rabbinate but about Nehome. My woman's sense can't understand what you are doing. Others will be ashamed to tell you so, but for Nehome's sake I don't care even if people say that I am insolent."

Reb Ore put down his spoon and said mildly: "On the contrary, Mehre, if I have really committed a wrong against Nehome, it's your duty to tell me."

128

"Thank you, Rabbi, for saying so. But I would have had my say anyway; such is my nature. So where's justice? Here we are, just before the holidays. All summer no peasants come to town, and now that the harvesting is over and the peasants have a few pennies in their pockets and they come to town to buy something, and to have some garments made, what do you do now, after a summer of idleness? You leave home and go to Stollen to spend the holidays with the Rabbi. And you like your *mitzvos* done right. You go from Paritch to Stollen and back on foot, so as to have the additional merit of the effort. It will take you at least six weeks to get there and back. All this is very fine, but at whose expense are you doing it? You do it at the expense of Nehome and the children. You left them at God's mercy. Who will provide for them these six weeks? And what kind of a holiday will Nehome have with you away? I am only a simple woman, so I ask you, who are a Rabbi, is such a thing permissible? Is it right to perform a *mitzvoh* at the expense of one's wife and children?"

Mother's face was flushed with anger and excitement. Shimon suspected that she was also frightened at her own audacity. But the old man only sighed without lifting his head. He stared at the tablecloth and answered in a low voice.

"You are right, Mehre. You said the very words that are in my mind and give me no rest."

Mother had not expected this kind of answer and was confused a moment. But soon she regained her composure and declared triumphantly:

"In that case, why are you doing it?"

Reb Ore sighed and, still not lifting his head, he spoke:

"Mehre, they say that you are truly a woman of valor. You provide for your family comfortably. You will therefore understand what I am about to tell you.

"There are times when one gets fed up with sewing sheepskin coats for peasants. All summer I make ready-to-

129

wear peasant coats. I sew and I sew, and every day is so plain and uninspired that it becomes intolerable. One reaches a depth of degradation so that he feels he is losing the image of God. You must understand that the soul wants food just as the body does. Once a year I flee to the Rabbi. There I forget the worries about a livelihood. There are no weekdays there. There every day is Sabbath; every day is a holiday. I stay about two weeks with the Rabbi, more I do not allow myself, and my soul absorbs some of the holiness, and then I go back to the peasant coats. I want you to understand, Mehre, that the soul is also a living thing and requires nourishment."

"But, Rabbi," Mother protested, "at whose expense? That's what I want to know. Would you sit down at a table to eat and let Nehome and the children go hungry? On account of your soul Nehome has to blind herself at her sewing machine. You will have a holiday at the Rabbi's table, and Nehome's holiday will be spoiled. And Nehome is so young, and she has such a great burden to bear."

"Golden words, Mehre. You are speaking golden words," Reb Ore said patiently. "But do you think I deceived Nehome with nice words and false promises? Did I promise her silk dresses and chicken soup on weekdays, or even on holidays, when I married her? When Sore, of blessed memory, died, and I was left with five orphans, I began to look for a wife. A man must have someone to take care of the household. Nehome heard about it and came crying and complaining that she did not want her sister's children to have a stepmother. Now that I left the rabbinate, she said, who would marry me? Some sick old woman—that's what Nehome said—and she would take out her bitterness on the children. I listened to her and my hair stood on end. I understood what the girl was getting at. I looked at her and she was still almost a child herself, while I was already a graybeard. So I said to myself: 'Ore,' I said, 'don't allow a Jewish daughter to ruin her own life.'

130

" 'Nehome, my child,' I said to her, 'don't even think such things. I am an old man. Your sister, Sore, suffered enough even when I was a rabbi, and still more when I became a tailor. What do you want with an old man burdened with five children who does not earn enough to feed them? It is not right, what you want to do.'

"But she would not listen to me. She wept and said: 'I will not allow my sister's children to have a stepmother. I will do sewing, I will wash the floors in strangers' houses, and I will help feed the children.'

"And do you think, Mehre, that I agreed so easily? First I told her that I didn't want to remarry at all. So she started coming to the house every day, and she would stay all hours, and there is the prohibition against being alone with a woman. I begged her, 'Leave me alone; what kind of trouble are you trying to cook up? I am an old man. And besides, I am a restless person, and I go to the Rabbi every year, and my mind is on other matters.' But it was no use. She threatened to kill herself. So we were married. I do the best I can to feed the family, and now, thank God, there are eight of us, and it is hard to earn a living; so there are times when a man is overcome with all this. It's more than I can bear and I must get away for a few weeks. I know it isn't right, but I take this sin upon myself, otherwise one can descend into such melancholy from which there is no coming out again."

Reb Ore resumed eating and Mother left the room. She soon returned with a large plate on which were a sour pickle, a dish of sour milk mixed with cream, beigel and rolls. She placed these before Reb Ore and silently left the room.

Reb Ore finished eating, recited grace and began preparing for his journey. Mother came in from the kitchen and, entirely unlike her usual habit, she spoke haltingly.

"Reb Ore," she said, "I beg you to forgive my sharp words which I spoke before. It wasn't I who was speaking —it was my troubles that spoke out of my mouth. Life is hard, Reb Ore, very hard, and my misery has taught me to understand the hardships of others. Often I think that it isn't others I pity, but myself."

"I forgive you with complete forgiveness, Mehre. You didn't say anything untoward," Reb Ore consoled her. "But sin no more and do not complain about your luck. God has rewarded you for your suffering. Reb Mendel talked to me this morning after prayers about your Shimon. He praised him sky high."

"That's what I wanted," Mother said, "that you should test him. Here is a *Gemora* on the table."

"It is not necessary," Reb Ore reassured her. "You may depend on Reb Mendel. You know what he told me? He said that he couldn't teach him any more; Shimon doesn't belong in his heder any longer. He instructs him individually. But this isn't the best way. A boy must have friends with whom to study. Reb Mendel does his work well; he looks after Shimon. Last year he taught him all of *Tanna Debei Eliahu*, and more recently Shimon began studying *Mishnaios* by himself. But a boy must study in a group. Let him go to Reb Getzel's heder."

Mother gasped: "I can't afford it, Reb Ore. Reb Getzel teaches only a handful of pupils, and he charges thirty rubles a season."

"About this you don't have to worry—God provides the tuition," Reb Ore reassured her.

"He will no doubt provide," Mother said bitterly. "I will bake another double batch of beigel. God hasn't been feeding us with butter rolls so far."

Reb Ore lifted his bundle to his back and started toward the door. He stopped at the threshold and turned to Mehre:

"Have faith. Let Shimon go to Reb Getzel's heder. I know that God will provide."

He kissed the *mezuzah* and left the house. Mother followed him with her eyes a long while, then she returned to the kitchen. She was upset, and for a while her perplexity expressed itself in vigorously banging her rakes against the floor of the oven. But she was too articulate to remain silent long, and soon she again engaged in her usual debate with God.

"If only I could confront Him and have my say before Him. I know He would be right in the end, for He no doubt knows what He is doing. But I would ask Him: Why is it that a saint like Reb Ore has to struggle for his livelihood while a shaven-faced pig like Lebke Polak rolls in luxury.

When Mother talked to God in this vein, Shimon never interfered; but this time he could not restrain himself and asked: "Mother, and what about the hereafter?"

"The hereafter?" Mehre said. "The rich have luck; he might take a notion to repent a minute before his death, when no time will be left for sinning, and so he will have it good both in this life and in the hereafter. You don't know how far a rich man's luck goes."

Shimon couldn't restrain his admiration. "You should have studied *Gemora*, Mother," he said. "You can find answers to any question."

Mother sighed. "Oh, if only I had been born a man. But you are lucky. You are a man and you have a good head. So find out what makes the world as it is, why there are so many wrongs. Find out. There are so many books and they are closed to me; I can barely find my way in the women's prayer book. But you can read even Rashi script. Find out everything, and see to it there shouldn't be so many wrongs. It is unthinkable that there is no purpose or reason beyond all this."

Shimon gaped at his mother. How did she read his mind? How did she guess the thoughts that were troubling him? How?

Shimon was suddenly recalled to the world of reality. Before Passover the town became deeply troubled with apprehensions of impending danger. A pogrom was expected almost daily. Mother rushed Rochel-Leah, Breine, and Shimon to Azarich.

Shimon's stay in Azarich became indelibly etched in his memory. Here he discovered that he belonged to a tribe. Here lived Uncle Matus, Uncle David, and Aunt Frade, and here too was Grandmother and a host of cousins. Shimon was trundled around from one relative's house to the other; he was petted and praised. He was particularly befriended by Avrom-Chaim, Aunt Frade's husband, a thin, stooped, youngish man with a face covered with freckles. He was the scholar of the family and he treated Shimon as an equal. On the second day after Shimon's arrival, he engaged him in learned conversation and confided to him:

"So, they say you have a good head. But the question is, will you remain a student? Do you understand what I mean? It is one thing to be learned and an entirely different matter to continue one's studies. A scholar may be likened to a thief. A thief is not one who knows how to steal, but one who actually steals. It is hard to remain a student all one's life. Much depends on what happens to you. If, after you are married, you will end up the way

134

I did, and have to worry about a living—well, you see for yourself. I used to know thoroughly several tractates of the Talmud, and I also was familiar with such works as *The Guide for the Perplexed* and the *Kuzari*. And now! The point is, what does one do with one's scholarship? That's what counts."

Avrom-Chaim talked to Shimon in this manner as he stood behind his shop counter waiting for customers. Shimon didn't quite understand what his uncle was aiming at. He realized that he was discontented, but did not know why. Surely, from the standpoint of material comfort, Avrom-Chaim seemed to live in luxury, compared to conditions in Shimon's home.

In Azarich, Shimon was also much impressed by the Bes Midrash which was crowded every evening. The place remained brilliantly lighted till very late. In Shimon's home town, the synagogue was crowded only during the evening prayers, whereas in Azarich it truly came to life only after the evening prayers. Then nearly the entire male population came here to study, some in groups, others individually, and some young men remained all night.

More than a year had passed since Shimon had begun studying *Mishnaios* by himself. Before going to Azarich, Shimon had promised Reb Mendel that he would review the entire Order *Zeraim*. He kept his promise.

One afternoon, as he was thus engaged, he was interrupted by Zorach. Shimon was standing at his Uncle David's lectern, reciting the strange text and swaying enthusiastically. "One does not plant different kinds of trees together," he read, "nor does one mix different kinds of vegetables." The text troubled Shimon. Compared to the intricacies of *Gemora*, Mishna was an easy subject. But the names of the different plants were strange to him. Who could tell what the ancient Hebrew names meant? He might learn the entire text by heart, yet should he have

135

occasion to sow the seeds of different plants, he might sow seeds whose mixing was forbidden.

Shimon was anxious to finish this part of *Zeraim* where he understood barely one out of every ten terms and to reach more comprehensible texts, when he suddenly sensed that someone was standing behind his back. He raised his head and saw that it was Zorach the Madman, a man about thirty years of age, with a short black beard and *peos* of dubious length. Zorach wore a long caftan, and his cap rested on the back of his head. His eyes shifted restlessly, but now he smiled at Shimon.

"So," he began, "the prodigy from Kalinkovich is still studying *Mishnaios*."

"He talks sense," Shimon couldn't help thinking; all scholars spoke with disdain of the straightforward texts of the Mishna. And he answered:

"This too is God's Torah. I promised my Rebbe to review the Order *Zeraim* while I am here."

"They say you are a prodigy," Zorach remarked, "only eleven years old and already a scholar."

"I don't know about that," Shimon replied. "I want to learn, that's all I know."

"Modest, too, not like other prodigies," Zorach laughed.

"I am not modest," Shimon blushed. "I am still a heder boy, and there are many things I can't understand."

"In that case your uncle Avrom-Chaim is a liar; he claimed that you know two volumes of the Talmud thoroughly."

Shimon was silent.

"I suppose you wonder how I know what your uncle has been saying?" Zorach continued. "I know everything that is said everywhere. I also know the Talmud better than anybody else in town. But I prefer to collect broken glass in the market place."

Shimon was intrigued. Everybody said that Zorach was mad. Yet he seemed to talk sense. So he asked him: "Why?"

136

"Because anyone who has sense must be mad. I thought for such a long time that things began to get mixed up in my head. Everybody lives a lie. They talk about the Torah but they don't observe it. When it suits their convenience they distort its meaning. I couldn't do it, because truth is truth and a lie is a lie, and the two can't be mixed; but if they can be mixed, then why be sane? Do you get what I mean?"

"Not entirely," Shimon admitted.

"So let me show you what I mean," Zorach said. He quickly began taking from his pockets pieces of broken glass and placed them on the lectern. They were of all shapes and colors. He arranged them in some kind of order and said: "Look well, now, these are the jewels of the High Priest's breastplate, just as they are listed in the Torah."

Shimon curiously examined the pieces of glass. Zorach had made his little speech with so much semblance of conviction, that he felt something might be gained by arguing with him. "I am surprised," Shimon therefore said, "that an intelligent and educated man like you should maintain that plain pieces of glass are jewels."

"There's reason in what I say," Zorach reassured him. "I want to prove to the entire world that if it is permissible to pervert the plain commandments of the Torah, then one may with equal reason maintain that pieces of glass are jewels."

"But who is perverting the words of the Torah?" Shimon asked.

"Who, you ask?" Zorach retorted. "Everybody does it. First the *Gemora,* then Rambam, then *Even Haezer,* and after them all the rabbis."

Shimon stared at him with open mouth. Zorach scooped up the pieces of glass and put them in his pocket, then he ran to the bookshelves and soon returned with an armful of volumes. He quickly opened a Bible and began to read pointing to the text with his fingers: " 'And if a man

137

seduce a virgin that is not betrothed and lies with her, he shall take her unto wife. But should her father refuse to give her to him for a wife, the man must give to the father silver equal to the dowry of a virgin.' This is what the Torah says. Now, tell me, does the Torah say that if the man refuses to marry the woman he can expiate his guilt with silver?"

Shimon was silent, and Zorach shouted: "Tell me, is that what the Torah says?"

"No," Shimon conceded.

"And now look in Kesubos, page thirty-nine, and in Rambam, and in *Even Haezer*. They say the exact opposite, that if the seducer refuses to marry the girl, he should be made to pay a fine of money and no more. Now what do you say to such an abomination?"

Shimon stared at him in surprise. "So what do you want?" he asked. "And if the *Gemora* or the Rambam appears to contradict the Torah, is that reason to get mad at the whole world? There must be some explanation."

Zorach looked at Shimon approvingly. He moistened his dry lips with the tip of his tongue and declared: "Still a boy, not even Bar Mitzvah yet, and talks such good sense. Others say I am crazy when I state my arguments, but not he."

A number of people entered the synagogue and looked with wonder at Zorach and Shimon engaged in pleasant conversation. But Zorach became tense at their arrival and said to Shimon: "Come, let us go for a walk. I want to tell you a strange story. Let's go before someone throws a wet towel at me."

They left the synagogue and Shimon followed Zorach. The street was quiet. Zorach led the way to the river where they sat down on a rock. They did not speak for a while. Zorach took pieces of glass from his pocket and skillfully bounced them off the surface of the water. When he exhausted his supply of glass, he began talking.

"It is bad," he said, "when one can't forget. It is a misfortune to remember too much. Do you suppose that I don't know that there is an explanation for the apparent contradiction between Rambam and the *Gemora* and the Torah? Of course I know, and some day I will tell it to you and you will enjoy it. But if only I could forget."

"Forget what, Reb Zorach?"

"If only I could forget my older brother, the scoundrel. Do you know who my family is? We are descended from the true Horowitzes. My father can trace his descent for four hundred years, and all his forebears were rabbis or men of wealth. My father is in the lumber business, and he comes here twice a year, before Pesach and before the Days of Awe. Fourteen years ago we lived in Petrokov. I was sixteen years old then and studied in the yeshiva; and my older brother, Gershon, was nineteen years old. They were arranging a match for him, and one day I received a letter by messenger to return home as the entire family was about to go to Bobroisk to celebrate Gershon's engagement. The bride-to-be was a great beauty and of good family, as she was descended from rabbis. She also knew Polish and Russian, and her father was wealthy. Altogether it was a fitting match for a Horowitz.

"I returned home to participate in the festivities, but instead of joy, I found the household in mourning. Mother went about the house, her eyes swollen from crying; Father nervously plucked his beard, and my brother Gershon went about like a lost soul.

"I realized that something had gone wrong, but they would not tell me what had happened. But when Thursday came and the wagons drew up in front of the house to take us to Bobroisk, the widow Beile-Chaye came running, together with her daughter, Elke, who had served as a maid in our house. She raised an outcry and screamed so that all the neighbors came running. 'Look, everybody,' she shouted. 'Look and see how this apostate ruined my daughter!'

"The entire town came running. The widow's relatives

came with axes and smashed the wheels of the wagons that stood ready to take us to Bobroisk. Elke's head and face were wrapped in a shawl, but her protruding belly announced her condition to all. The trip to Bobroisk was called off, and our house became a place of mourning.

"I did not know what to do with myself. I was angry at Father, at Gershon, at Mother who constantly shed tears. What were they crying about? Why were they mourning? The law was clear: Gershon had to marry Elke. At first I didn't dare talk about this to Father, but I did argue with Gershon. 'Is it possible?' I asked him. 'Have you no heart? The law is as clear as clear can be, and besides, it is a pity on the orphan girl. She is also very beautiful, so what is the great misfortune? That she isn't so well-born?'

"But Gershon insisted that he could not marry her. And though he did not deny that he had seduced her, he insisted that he now hated her, couldn't bear to look at her.

"I gave him no rest. 'What do you mean?' I argued. 'First you loved her, and now you hate her?'

"'Why are you surprised?' he countered. 'Isn't it written of Amnon that after he lay with Tamar he came to hate her with a hatred greater than the love he had at first felt for her?'

"'What kind of comparison is that?' I demanded. 'In the Bible the story concerns a prince and a princess, and Absalom did in fact kill Amnon for his sin. But you have wronged an orphan, and now she is pregnant. What will she do with your bastard?'

"'We will compensate her,' Gershon said.

"That Saturday Elke's relatives halted the reading of the Torah in the synagogue until Father consented to a trial. That same day I summoned my courage and said to Father at the dinner table: 'Father, there is a clear law in the Torah concerning what should be done in a case like this. So where is justice?'

140

"But Father only flew into a rage. He pounded the table and shouted: 'Silence! I know what the law is, and nobody asked you to pass judgment.'

"I left the table in anger. What was happening to my pious father and to my kind mother! How could they see the sorrow of an orphan and not commiserate with her!

"That afternoon I reviewed all the laws dealing with seduction, and I saw that Father and my brother would get off with a mere fine. I became very angry and I flung the *Gemora* and Rambam and the other volumes on the floor. I carried on; I smashed dishes until Father locked me in a room. He did not release me till after the trial.

"Elke was awarded twelve hundred rubles and continuing support of the child. I became despondent. I ate little and refused to change my clothes. They paid no attention to me. I did not go back to the yeshiva.

"But people's memories are short. Elke went to another city and my parents again looked for a suitable match for Gershon. One fine day he returned from Homlie sporting a fine watch—a gift from his new bride-to-be. Father was satisfied and Mother was happy.

"When I saw the watch I felt as if something moved in my brain. I began shouting to Gershon: 'Adulterer! You are an adulterer! And you, Father, won't get off so easy either. Do you think God will overlook the tears of a widow and an orphan?'

"I flew into a rage and smashed everything in sight before they bound me with ropes.

"I was taken to doctors, and they pronounced me insane. But I knew I was not insane. I wanted to do something to spite Father and Mother and Gershon. I wanted to humble them publicly. Do you think my mind wasn't clear when they had me bound and poured cold water on my head? I was aware of everything, and planned to do the family some great spite.

"It occurred to me that I could become an apostate—I could run off and become an apostate. But the thought of becoming a Goy made me vomit violently. The doctors could not figure out the cause of my vomiting. How could I explain it to them?

"Finally I was put in an insane asylum abroad. I continued to plan humiliation for my family. I finally decided to pretend non-violent insanity. In this manner I would not have to observe the laws of Judaism which my family perverted, and I would not become a Goy either.

"When I was brought back from abroad, Father moved to this town, where no one knew us. He told everyone that I lost my reason from too much studying."

Shimon listened breathlessly to Zorach's tale. It sounded rational. When Zorach finished, Shimon said: "You know, Reb Zorach, it seems to me that you talk good sense."

Zorach looked at him mildly: "My, but you understand a lot for a little boy! For a long time now I've been sorry about the whole business. But how does one become sane all of a sudden?"

Shimon laughed. "Is this also a problem? Do now as you wish, just as you did then."

Zorach smiled agreement. "It's an idea," he conceded.

They were silent for a while. Zorach bounced pebbles off the surface of the water. The sun was setting and Shimon rose to go. "I will miss *Minhah* if I don't hurry back," he said.

"Go," Zorach agreed. "I will stay here and enjoy another few hours of madness. Tomorrow morning I will start being sane again."

Uncle Avrom-Chaim stood behind the counter in his shop and talked to Shimon:

"He probably told you that the *Gemora* and Rambam and all the commentators misinterpret the Bible."

"He did," Shimon admitted.

"He showed you his pieces of glass and told you the story of the seduced orphan? You must think you are the first one to hear his story. But it isn't so. He tells it to every new person in town. When I first came here as a son-in-law, he told me the same tale. I tried to show him that the commentators were right, and he flew into a rage. Did you argue with him?"

"I couldn't argue with him. I haven't studied the laws dealing with seduction," Shimon said.

"Then bear in mind, Shimon, that the entire story about his brother is pure imagination. Nothing to it. Zorach lost his mind from too much studying. He knew the entire Talmud by the time he was sixteen years old."

At this point Grandmother took a hand in the conversation. "You, Avrom-Chaim," she said, "believe Zorach's father, but I believe Zorach himself. He tells the truth. Did you know the Horowitzes before they came to Azarich?"

Avrom-Chaim shrugged his shoulders. "Women love romantic tales," he said.

The following morning all Azarich was agog with the news that Zorach came to the synagogue, took his place at his father's permanent seat and put on phylacteries. This was the first time he had been seen participating in the morning prayers in the traditional manner. But his pocket still bulged with pieces of glass.

A week later Shimon returned home.

21. *Eliokim-Getzel*

Eliokim-Getzel, Shimon's next teacher, was rated the best *Gemora* instructor in town. He was not a native of Kalinkovich. Many years earlier he had been brought to town to tutor the sons of the richest man thereabouts, and he was thus engaged for five years. When his charges grew up, he set up a school of his own. Behind his back he was called Reb Getzel, but to his face he was invariably addressed by his full name as Reb Eliokim-Getzel, or simply as Rebbe.

At the time Shimon knew him, Reb Getzel was a lanky, tall old man with a white beard tinted a shade of green, black, deeply set eyes and strangely long fingers. His exact age at this time was not known. Reb Getzel himself conceded that he had already reached seventy, but people in town surmised that he was closer to eighty than to seventy. Despite his ripe age, Reb Getzel stood erect and wore no glasses. He lectured regularly before the local Talmud society, took an active part in communal affairs, and maintained his reputation as the best *Gemora* teacher in town.

Everybody in town respected him. Indeed, more than half the finest citizens in the community had been his pupils at one time or another, and all of them had retained, together with their respect for him, also a tinge of fear.

144

For more than forty years Reb Getzel had taught *Gemora* in Kalinkovich. At one time he would accept no pupils younger than thirteen, unless they were prodigies, and he kept them until they married or left town to attend a yeshiva. But times changed. Boys stopped studying earlier, and by the time Shimon joined his class, Reb Getzel accepted pupils as young as eleven.

There had been a time when it was a great honor to be Reb Getzel's pupil. It was also an advantage when matchmaking time came. However, times changed and the prestige of being Reb Getzel's pupil diminished—but it did not altogether disappear. Even in Shimon's day a boy who was accepted in Reb Getzel's heder was considered exceptional.

It was Reb Getzel's custom never to have more than ten pupils at a time—six from rich homes and four from poor. The rich paid thirty rubles a season; the poor as much as they could afford, but no matter how little they paid the tuition was higher than with any other teacher.

Two other boys from Reb Mendel's heder went to Reb Getzel together with Shimon. All three were in some trepidation on the first morning of the new semester, and agreed to meet on the corner and to enter at the same time.

They found themselves in a spacious room in the middle of which stood a long red table surrounded by eleven chairs. The three new pupils were the first arrivals and did not know what to do. Since they had not yet said their morning prayers, they decided to do so, as had been their custom in Reb Mendel's heder.

Some minutes later, Reb Getzel and the other pupils came in. When the other boys saw the newcomers thus occupied, they laughed. Reb Getzel silenced them, and when the three new boys had finished their prayers, he told them: "Children, you should know that this is not a beginners' school. You must say your prayers before you

145

come here." He then tested their stock of knowledge. It was a strange quiz. He asked each boy which subject in the *Gemora* he knew best and told him to recite. He did not interfere with the recitation, nor did he correct their errors. After they had finished, he announced briefly: "The three of you will start with tractate *Berakhos*."

At lunch time, Reb Getzel asked the three newcomers to remain. After the other pupils had left, he addressed his new charges as follows: "I purposely asked you to stay, because I want to talk to you, as I always do to new pupils. I want you to realize that in my school you don't have to depend on me. You will have to do your own studying. I will only observe you, and see to it that you do not deceive yourselves. But if you do not apply yourselves to your studies, it will be your loss. It is the duty of a teacher to be like a spring—willing to give refreshing water to all who want it. How much each drinks from the spring depends on his thirst and his capacity. The three of you have good heads. You can study by yourselves. I want you to learn a page of the *Gemora* each day—half a page if it happens to be a long one. I will test you three times a week. It will depend on you whether I keep the three of you in one group. If you will not deceive yourselves or me, you will remain in one group; otherwise I will have to separate you. And now you can go home for lunch."

The boys were free. They could do as they pleased. They could study or not, just as they wished. Even when they did not do well in their tests, Reb Getzel showed no anger. He would merely remark drily: "You're wasting time."

Much time was, indeed, being wasted. Shimon learned to play cards, and a button game. He learned to skate. He spent much time listening to stories, and relating some himself. The older boys smoked. Two of the older boys brought tobacco from their fathers' stores. Shimon learned to smoke.

146

Four weeks passed in this manner. Then Shimon was overcome with remorse. "What was he doing?" he began asking himself. "Mother was proud of him. His brothers and sisters looked up to him. The entire family showed him off admiringly—the sole scholar in the tribe. Yet he was deceiving them all. He was cheating. And what would come of all this?"

One afternoon, when Reb Getzel sat engrossed in some volume, Shimon silently seated himself before him and waited expectantly. Reb Getzel became aware of him. He closed his book, took a pinch of snuff, smiled, and said: "Well, what is troubling you? I see you want to say something, so go ahead and speak."

Shimon stammered: "Rebbe, I am wasting my time. I am cheating in my studies. It's a great wrong to my mother."

He stopped, unable to go on. There was a lump in his throat and he was on the verge of tears. He managed to swallow the lump and added: "I want to study, but I can't. I can't rely on myself."

Reb Getzel looked long at the boy's contrite face. "Listen to what I will tell you," he finally began. "It will be quite a speech. First of all I want you to know that you have told me nothing new. I know very well what is going on in my school. And secondly I want you to know that I intentionally put you to the test. The Midrash says: It is written in the Torah 'And God tested Abraham,' to teach us that only the righteous, who will not easily stray, are put to the test. Likewise, Rabbi Yonah told a parable: When flax is beaten, its quality is improved. But this is true only when one starts with good flax. If the flax is of an inferior quality, it is merely crumbled in the threshing. I had expected you to come sooner. I knew you would get tired of wasting your time. But you held out for four weeks.

"There are two ways to teach pupils. One way consists in stuffing them as one would stuff an ox that was being fattened. The other way is for the teacher to withhold his

147

knowledge from a poor student, and to lavish it generously on the good student. I like to follow the second way."

Shimon did not understand what Reb Getzel was aiming at. The old man continued:

"I have been a teacher for nearly fifty years. How many scholars do you think I have brought up? And when I say scholars I do not mean Jews who have studied much. We have many such. By scholars I mean those whose way of life, whose souls, whose every breath is Torah. There aren't many such. And do you know why? Because God created the world with much lavishness. See for yourself. For the sake of one flower He created an entire bush. For the sake of a few apples He created an entire tree with deep roots and a thick trunk and many branches and thousands of leaves and millions of blossoms. The Midrash says that a teacher is like a woman who sets a brooding hen on many eggs, of which only a few hatch. Another Midrash declares: Thousands learn to read the Scriptures; hundreds learn the Mishna; of each hundred, not more than ten study *Gemora;* and of these ten only one becomes fit to interpret the law and to pass judgment."

Shimon listened to all this and wondered: "What was Reb Getzel driving at?" His perplexity was soon resolved.

"You have a good head," Reb Getzel concluded. "Your abilities are not as great as those of Ephraim-David. But he comes from a family of scholars, and is not much impressed by the Torah, whereas you are the sole student in your entire family, and learning is a revelation to you. You can therefore become the one for whom I have been waiting all my life.

"You will therefore do as follows. You will start to study *Pesahim,* by yourself. Avrom-Moishe will test you every day. You will come to me every morning, two hours before prayers, and we will study *Yore Deiah.* We will begin with the laws governing milk and meat. I have my reasons for this. And on your own you will continue study-

148

ing *Mishnaios*. You should also look into the Scriptures. Now you will have more than enough work. You will also wait on me. Whether you will be satisfied with me, or I with you, remains to be seen. In all my life I have used this system of teaching with only five pupils. You will be the sixth. Of the five, three were a total waste of time— lost effort; the fourth is a famous man in Paris—he even changed his Jewish name; the fifth remained a great scholar and a still greater pauper. Now, tell me, what do you think of such an outcome?"

"I will come tomorrow morning," Shimon said.

Shimon spent two-and-a-half years with Reb Getzel. The first year-and-a-half was a time of great and joyous diligence. The remaining year was marked by too many interruptions and hardships. But the entire period left a more profound mark on him than the three years he had spent with Reb Mendel.

The great happiness and the purposefulness of that time remain most clearly etched in Shimon's mind. The days were well-ordered. In the mornings, after the prayers, he applied himself to the tractate *Pesahim*. In the afternoons, Avrom-Moishe, who was two-and-a-half years his senior, heard him recite his morning assignment. The two soon became fast friends. Though Shimon had a quicker grasp and a better memory than his mentor, the latter excelled in depth, and restrained his younger charge in his eagerness. Finished with the daily assignment, Shimon studied *Mishnaios*, and in the evenings he read the Scriptures. He loved the Mishna more than the *Gemora*, and sensed a close kinship between the Mishna and the code of laws of the *Yore Deiah* which Reb Getzel taught him each morning.

The early morning sessions frequently were no more than monologues by Reb Getzel. Shimon remembers one of these, which was held about a week after the morning sessions began. Reb Getzel said:

"First I want you to understand why I teach you the

149

Yore Deiah. I want to show you that the study of the Torah is not for the sake of gaining mental keenness. The Torah must have a basis in real life; it must be linked with deeds. And secondly I want to show you that you are in too much of a hurry, you try to grasp too much. I want to tell you an anecdote that contains a great truth. It is told of Reb Chaim-Leib, the famous prodigy of Sosnowitz, that a young man famed as a scholar once came to visit him. As is the custom among scholars, they discussed matters pertaining to learning. When the young visitor left, the prodigy of Sosnowitz was asked: 'Well, Rabbi, what is your opinion of him?' But the prodigy of Sosnowitz only sighed and answered: 'He is a great scholar indeed, but he wastes so much time studying that he has no time left to learn anything.'

"You, too, try to grasp too much. Yet it is written in the Scriptures that he who hastes to get rich will end badly. Where study is concerned, it is not quantity that counts. It is better to know one subject well than to know an entire tractate superficially. If you know your one subject well, you have acquired a key to the entire Oral Law."

In two months Shimon learned all the laws governing the salting of meat, a total of forty pages in *Yore Deiah.* Then he came to the section dealing with the rules governing the separation of meat from dairy dishes. At this point Reb Getzel told him to proceed on his own, and to follow the path of simple interpretation. To make sure that Shimon had grasped the spirit as well as the letter of the laws, Reb Getzel asked him to give him a written digest of each law. This was Shimon's first literary assignment, and to this day he has retained the habit of making marginal notes in all the books he reads.

But even though Shimon now pursued his study of *Yore Deiah* by himself, he continued coming to Reb Getzel's house each morning. Teacher and pupil would then sit at opposite ends of the table, each engrossed in his own volume. The old teacher loved to have the young and eager boy at his side. Perhaps it reminded him of his own youth. Besides, Shimon also waited on him; he handed him a glass of tea; he brought him a book from the shelves; or ran an errand for him.

Reb Getzel also was active in communal matters, and frequently took a hand in settling disputes, righting wrongs, and guiding strayed souls to the paths of righteousness.

Early one morning, shortly after dawn, Reb Getzel said to Shimon: "Run to Leibke the Tinsmith and tell him that I want to have a chat with him."

Leibke the Tinsmith was a man about sixty-five years old. Broad-shouldered, powerful, with a jet black beard, his entire body breathed strength. He no longer worked at his trade, ever since his eyesight had begun to fail. But as a matter of habit he was still called "the Tinsmith" in town. He now derived his livelihood from buying discarded metal at the railroad station, mostly lead which had been used to seal the freight cars. When he bought lead, usually between twenty and thirty pounds, he used to carry it in the bosom of his crude linen shirt. Other metals he carried to town in a sack on his back. His hands were like a bear's paws, and when he greeted anyone and good-humoredly pressed his hand, the one greeted doubled over with pain, to Leibke's delight. "A generation made of straw," he would sneer.

Leibke was inordinately pious. On his way to and from the railway station he used to recite Psalms. On Saturdays he never took a rapid step, to avoid even the semblance of exerting effort on the holy day. On days when he ate meat he did not touch dairy dishes at all.

Though in town Leibke was considered as a bit of a simpleton, he was nevertheless universally loved, for he was particular not only in observing commandments regarding relations between man and God; he likewise ob-

151

served, with equal severity, the commandments affecting relations between man and man. It was known in town that no sick and lonely pauper would remain untended with Leibke around—he was bound to come to visit him, and would probably also provide the medicine, as well as a piece of chicken. And when it was necessary to spend a night at the bedside of a critically sick man, Leibke could always be counted on, even though he had not spent the preceding three nights at home. The town also did not forget that Leibke was the best *masseur*. When a cholera epidemic broke out some years earlier, Leibke spent four consecutive days and nights rubbing with alcohol those afflicted. During those four days he lived on alcohol and egg rolls. He took the alcohol because it was believed to have immunizing effects against cholera, and he ate egg rolls because it was not necessary to wash one's hands before, nor to recite grace after eating them—only a brief blessing was required and he could thus refresh himself without diverting time from his urgent labors.

Leibke was a friendly and affectionate soul, but in matters of piety he was uncompromising and would not listen even to the Rabbi. Whenever the Rabbi of Kalinkovich tried to ease his discipline, he would answer briefly: "I don't look for indulgence."

Leibke had an only son, Shaie, who went to America. For a long time nothing was heard from him. But at the time when Shimon was a pupil of Reb Getzel, Shaie began sending frequent letters to his parents, and also some money. Leibke breathed more easily. He didn't have to work as hard as before, but what was more important, he had a ready penny for charitable purposes.

This went on for some time, until Shaie sent his parents a photograph of himself in his new home. Leibke took one glance at the picture and stopped claiming the money orders which his son sent him. The mailman told Reb Getzel that nearly one hundred rubles were waiting for Leibke at the post office, but that he refused to claim them and preferred to earn his few pennies by buying old metal at the railway station.

When Shimon reached Leibke's house to ask him to come to Reb Getzel, he found him with sack on his back ready to go to the station. Informed of the summons, the tinsmith angrily turned to his wife: "Sarah, you informed on me to Reb Getzel? It won't do you a bit of good."

"May I not live to see grandchildren if I said as much as a word to him," Sarah vehemently denied the accusation.

Leibke muttered: "Oaths, all the time oaths. Woman! Who tells you to swear?" He thought a while, then ordered his wife: "Give me his fine portrait."

"What do you need his portrait for?"

"You won't be any the wiser if I tell you."

Shimon accompanied Leibke to Reb Getzel's house. Reb Getzel wasted no time, and as soon as they entered he said: "Leibke, I hear that you refuse to claim the money which your only son sent you. Is that possible?"

Leibke took out the young man's photograph and put it on the table. "Here, look at him," he muttered. "The image of God is gone from his face—a face smooth as a kneading board."

"Is he by any chance the only Jew who shaves?" Reb Getzel asked.

"He is not only shaven. I hear that he also eats *treif*, and doesn't observe the Sabbath. I don't want to benefit from his money. He is trying to bribe me with his kindness."

Reb Getzel smiled. "You hear that he does this, that and some other thing. People talk. How do you know that all this is true? But let us assume for a moment that it is all true. What of it? Do you think that your son is no longer a Jew on account of it? That he is outside the community of Israel?"

"May he live and enjoy good health within the community of Israel," Leibke said. "But I don't want to have any dealings with him."

Reb Getzel became angry. "You are cruel, Leibke. You are a cruel man. Let us say that he is a great sinner, but here is one commandment—honoring Father and Mother— which he wants to observe. But you will not allow him to do so. You insist that when your only son will (one hundred and twenty years from now) face his Creator, he should do so barren of good deeds. In that case, what will save him from purgatory? Is it right on your part? Is it fair? You have a kind heart, you help the poor; but where your only son is concerned, you become heartless."

Leibke listened to this harangue with open mouth. He thought a while, then he announced: "Rabbi, you have me confused. I want to think the matter over."

After this meeting Leibke again claimed his son's offer- ings.

Whenever Reb Getzel went to communal events, he took Shimon with him. Shimon thus had an opportunity to attend meetings, trials, public disputes. Reb Getzel said that he needed Shimon to escort him through the unlit streets. Shimon now suspects that it was an alibi, that Reb Getzel wanted him to be present at these functions as part of his education.

That spring the town was in turmoil. It was the eve of Passover. The melting snows damaged the roof of the poor- house and undermined its walls. Most of its windows lacked some panes, and the doors hung precariously. The place had not been whitewashed in five years. But there was no money for repairs. The preceding autumn the community had brought a doctor to town for the first time in its history. He was to be paid eight hundred rubles a year and a contract was signed with him for three years. This obli- gation consumed the entire income from the bath house, the slaughter house and from the donation boxes. There was much arguing and shouting, but no source of funds could be uncovered to repair the tottering poorhouse. And

154

then Passover came close, and it was necessary to give thought to providing matzos for the poor in town.

As the situation became critical, Reb Getzel sent Shimon to call Nachum Falk and Yankel the carpenter. Nachum Falk had six grown sons, and Yankel the carpenter also a man of strength, had five sons. When they came, Reb Getzel addressed them briefly: "Let it remain a secret known only to us, but next Saturday, immediately after the prayers, you will take the *taleisim* from everyone."

Nachum Falk objected: "Yankel may have no trouble doing it in the new Bes Midrash, but how can I get away with it in the old synagogue? You know that Leibe Poliak, the *gabbai*, is a rich man, and half the town earns its living from him, and he doesn't like it when something is done without his knowledge. It may lead to fights."

Reb Getzel smiled. "Nachum Falk," he said, "you're getting old. There was a time when you weren't afraid of such things, especially when a good cause was involved. But don't worry. I will stand by you. You will take up the *taleisim* and give them to me, and I will hand them to your sons, and they will put them on the table on the reading platform. To avoid a quarrel, I will inform Leibe Poliak about it beforehand."

When the time came, no one resisted having his *tallis* taken. Nachum Falk's sons guarded the *taleisim* on the synagogue table all that day. In the evening everyone came to ransom his *tallis*, and there was enough money to repair the poorhouse.

Shimon remembers his surprise that even the *tallis* of Isaac "white head," a poor man who lived on charity, was taken up. "What could they get from such a pauper?" he argued with his mentor, Avrom-Moishe.

"You have a thick skull," Avrom-Moishe jeered at him. "Don't you understand? It was in order not to shame those who have no money."

For three consecutive days Reb Getzel's house was in turmoil. Leibe Poliak's two older sons, both former pupils of Reb Getzel, brought a lawsuit against two other merchants who were likewise alumni of Reb Getzel's heder. The litigants insisted that their former teacher be their judge, and demanded that he pass on the merits of their case according to the law and not seek to effect a compromise. What they wanted, they said, was not agreement, but the legal right and wrong of their case. Shimon was present during the trial and it was his duty to write down the arguments, and to bring the books that Reb Getzel asked for. But at the end of three days, Reb Getzel pronounced a compromise judgment.

Both parties objected volubly. "We refuse to accept the judgment," they cried. "We told you, Rabbi, that we would rather lose the case, just so we know who is right and who isn't."

Reb Getzel lost his patience and pounded on the table. "Silence, brats! What kind of talk is this! You want me to judge who is entirely right? Only God is altogether right, but even to Him the prophet said, 'Thou art just, Oh Lord, yet will I dispute with you.' Besides God no one is entirely right."

The litigants were not cowed. "But, Rabbi," they protested, "we cannot accept your compromise decision. The business world will . . ."

This only exasperated Reb Getzel still further. "Silence, I said," he shouted. "What? You won't abide by my judgment? Never in my life have I raised a hand against any man, but now, big as you are, I will slap you. Do you think I have the strength to put up with your stubbornness? You deserve to be fined for your insolence. But I too deserve to be fined for having raised such pupils. I hereby impose a fine upon myself which I will pay to the Society to Aid the Sick."

The four bearded men, fathers of grown children, felt ashamed. Keen businessmen though they were, they wilted under Reb Getzel's anger. Seeing their discomfiture, Reb

Getzel softened. "Very well," he said, "let each of you give a Quarter and Shimon will go and get some whisky and egg rolls and we will drink *lehayim*. But remember, no anger and resentment against each other. This is also a part of my judgment."

The four men grinned.

Reb Getzel disdained hair-splitting logic. "Every question," he maintained, "can be answered if only one knows *Gemora* and Rashi's commentary.

One day Ephraim-Dovid, the most brilliant and scholarly young man in town, came to Reb Getzel and related triumphantly:

"Just listen to what happened, Rabbi. I went into the Bes Midrash and there was Reb Mordecai Kroll sitting with the Talmud Society, and he turned to page six of *Berakhos* and challenged them, 'It says here, These are the *tefillin* of the Holy One. And what is written in them? Who is like unto Thy people Israel, one nation in the world. To this *tosephes* says: That is why on the first day of Passover we read in the special prayers, the *tefillin* added glory to His crown. And now, you Kalinkovich scholars, who will tell me what is the question raised by *tosephes* and what is the meaning of the answer?'

"You understand, Rabbi," Ephraim-Dovid exulted, "he picked a moment when all the real scholars were not there. Those present clucked their tongues and didn't know what to answer. Then he saw me and asked if I knew the answer. And I gave him the answer at once. I said, 'The question is why in the Holy One's *tefillin* it says: Who is like unto *Thy* people Israel, when it should say: Who is like unto *My* people Israel. And the answer is that the *tefillin* themselves praise God.' I showed him what a pupil of Reb Getzel can do."

Reb Getzel looked at his brilliant pupil and sighed. "I suppose you want to be praised, but you don't deserve it. Reb Mordecai wanted to show off in the Bes Midrash, to prove that he deserved his dowry. But what are you so proud of? Had you stopped to think a moment you would have realized that the *tefillin* of the Holy One contain the same verses from the Torah as any other *tefillin,* and God will not change the words of the Torah in order to make them more understandable to us. And furthermore, do you think that God has an arm and a head on which to put on *tefillin,* like any mortal? Don't we say every morning that 'He has no body, nor any of the attributes of a body, and no image whatsoever'? Think it over. You have a keen mind. Or perhaps you are too keen for common sense understanding."

"Rabbi," Ephraim-Dovid agreed enthusiastically, "I get what you are aiming at. There is more keenness in your common sense than any amount of *pilpul.*"

Shimon recalls a stroll which Reb Getzel, Ephraim-Dovid, Avrom-Moishe and he took one day. They walked on the outskirts of town toward the forest, and passed by the cemetery. A sound of wailing was heard.

"The voice sounds familiar," Reb Getzel said. "It is the voice of my daughter-in-law. She went to visit my Brokhe's grave. What is she wailing there?"

As they came nearer, the words of the wailing woman were heard distinctly:

"Oh my saintly mother-in-law! Go at once to the Throne of Glory and appeal to the Holy One and tell Him that your grandson Borukh is about to be called for military service, and may He preserve him from falling into the hands of Goyim. Weep and implore His mercy, and do not leave Him until He grants your request. Remind Him of your saintliness and your prayers and your charity."

Reb Getzel spat in disgust. "Why, this is calling upon the dead, real necromancy."

"Rabbi," Ephraim-Dovid said, "but isn't the custom of visiting the graves of the dead mentioned many times in the Talmud? So how can you call this necromancy?"

158

"That's just the trouble with you," Reb Getzel sighed, "that your mind is too keen and you remember all the quotations. One goes to visit the graves of parents to be reminded of their good deeds and to have thoughts of repentance. But to call on the dead to intercede for us? This is the same as witchcraft. You know what, Ephraim-Dovid," he concluded, "it seems to me that as soon as you discover that all these old-wives' customs are so much nonsense, you will conclude that there is nothing to faith itself. You must learn to separate the chaff from the grain."

Reb Getzel's insight proved correct—at least so far as Ephraim-Dovid was concerned. His words entered Shimon's mind and germinated there for a long time until they bore fruit many years later.

This was a happy year and a half for Shimon; but the last year that he spent with Reb Getzel was marred by many troubles.

159

22. *Troubled Times*

During the first year and a half that Shimon attended Reb Getzel's heder, the material situation at home improved considerably. Three of the children helped with the baking. Gitte, the oldest daughter, worked alongside Mother. Simcha, the oldest son, sold the bakery goods in the market-place, and fourteen-year-old Rochel-Leah helped both at home and in the market-place. Shimon, the young scholar, was freed of all mundane duties. The family boasted of his devotion to his studies, and did not permit him to deviate from his course.

At this time Mother's earnings were considerable, and she did not complain about Father's meager income. "What he makes is just enough to pay the tuition," she used to say. "And he is well, thank God. What would I have done had God inflicted on me a sick or crippled husband? Even in misfortune it is good to have luck. Thank God for things as they are."

All at once everything changed. Gitte was married rather suddenly. A suitable match appeared unexpectedly—a heaven-sent match, Mother thought. In the neighborhood lived a young couple. The husband, a men's tailor and an excellent craftsman, was twenty-four years old. His wife died suddenly. Mehre at once decided that he was a fitting match for her oldest daughter. She knew his family. The young man's father was a *melamed* in Azarich. The young widower, on his part, was strongly attracted to beautiful, eighteen-year-old Gitte. Within a short time the marriage was arranged.

Mother planned carefully. She needed Gitte's help in the bakery for another two years, until Rochel-Leah could be of greater assistance. The young couple would therefore come to live with the bride's parents. Where would she make room for them? She had a ready answer. Four new rooms would be added to the house. The son-in-law had some money saved and he could contribute toward the cost of the construction. The entire family could then live together comfortably, and the young man could open a tailor shop right in the house.

But Mother's plans did not work out. After Gitte was married, she refused to get up early in the morning, and Mother could not command her as she had done before. A married daughter has to obey her husband, and not her mother. Mehre tried to appeal to her conscience.

"Daughter, you have left me in the lurch," she argued. "Remodeling the house cost a fortune, and I have to pay interest on the borrowed money. Rochel-Leah is too young to knead the dough. Haven't I done you a favor by marrying you off young? You have a fine husband, a good provider who loves you. Now have pity on your mother. Without your help I will collapse under the load—three school boys to maintain. Do you want your mother to die?"

Gitte listened, nodded agreement, promised to reform, and kept her promise a few days. Months passed in this manner. Mother lost her patience and began to shout and to curse. Then Gitte became pregnant, and her husband, Shmuel-Haim, severely ordered Mother to leave his wife alone. Mehre had a good cry, and submitted. She began to rise still earlier, and the bakery continued to operate as before.

Then came the trouble with Simcha, the oldest son. Mother dearly loved Simcha. He was a handsome, curly-haired, blue-eyed boy. He was very careful of his appearance, and Mother, who loved neatness in everything admired him for this trait. Simcha was born two months before Father went to serve in the army. For five years Mother worked hard as a seamstress to support her two children, and indeed, they lacked nothing. When Father returned from the service, he found two grown children and Mother in a secure position financially.

But Simcha was pampered and spoiled. He was disobedient and did not want to study. His abilities were considerable but he was not disciplined to use them. When he became thirteen years old, Mother took him out of heder and engaged a private tutor for him, but matters did not improve much.

After Gitte's marriage, Simcha had to shoulder a much heavier burden of work. Rochel-Leah could not relieve him from his post in the market-place as often as she did before, and he also had to rise earlier to help roll the beigel. Mother knew that he worked too hard, but she figured that this would not last more than a year and a half until the younger son, Shlomo, would be old enough to help and Rochel-Leah could be asked to undertake more difficult tasks. Then she planned to find for Simcha a post as apprentice salesman in a dry-goods store. A good salesman had to know Russian and be handy with figures. She therefore made a special effort and engaged a tutor for Simcha. But the boy rebelled against the yoke imposed on him. He always managed to fall asleep just as his tutor was due to arrive. Arguments, appeals, even blows proved of no avail. Finally the tutor became disgusted and gave up. Simcha was not especially despondent over this development. He merely stopped his afternoon naps. Then Mother realized that the boy's sleep had not been due to exhaustion, that something else was the matter, and she began to nag him for an explanation.

"Listen, Simcha," she would say, "you can't fool me. It's peculiar that sleep overcame you each time just as the tutor was about to arrive. Something else is the matter.

Tell me the truth and I will stop nagging you and eating my heart out."

"I want to become a tailor," Simcha blurted out. "Let me become an apprentice to Moishe the tailor."

This was a heavy blow to Mother. But she did not get angry; instead, she remonstrated gently: "I had thought that we had more than enough artisans in the family, that you would become a salesman, learn Russian and figuring; and now I see that you are drawn to the tailor's table."

"And how is Shmuel-Haim worse off without Russian and figuring?" Simcha remonstrated. "He has his own shop and two apprentices."

In the end Mother had to give in. Now she had only Rochel-Leah to help her with the baking. For a while she was at a loss what to do, then she solved her problem. Shimon stopped going to Reb Getzel early in the morning and helped Rochel-Leah. He soon learned to roll beigel and perform similar jobs; he could even knead a batch of dough if it was not too large. Rochel-Leah, not yet fifteen years old, had a double job. In the mornings she worked in the bakery and later in the day she took Simcha's stand in the market-place. Shimon tended to the selling outside till about ten o'clock each morning.

But this arrangement did not work out well. Two children had to do the work of three grown ups. The most difficult labor was reserved for Mother, and as a result she was always nervous, tense and depressed. She suffered keenly that Shimon's studies were interrupted, and she vented her anger on Father who did not seem to take it to heart. It was all her fault, he argued. "You always reach for the sky," he said. "You forget that you are the wife of a shoemaker, a pauper who can't support such a large family, may no evil eye befall it. Now I ask you, is it my fault that I am poor? Other artisans who have children have it much easier, if only they use their heads—as soon as the children get a little older they are taken to the work bench. Elie has two sons working in his shop, and Eisik has

163

three. As soon as they learned to say their prayers, they were taken into the shop. But you!" and at this point Father only waved his hand in a gesture of despair. "I am sick and tired of talking about it. The older one you wanted to turn into a salesman, and if not a salesman then a tailor; the younger one you insist must be a scholar. When did we ever have scholars in the family? One did become a rabbi of sorts, so he got tired of it and became a tailor, like his father."

To this Mother would answer sarcastically: "Look whom he's trying to imitate, Elie and Eisik the shoemakers! Why don't you try to imitate Moishe Dvoire's, or Haim Gildi's? Some fault he found with me—that I want to do right before God and man; and all he wants is to be like other shoemakers. If I had depended on you we'd long ago have had to take charity."

"Mehre!" Father would raise his voice at this point, "I don't want to be like Moishe Dvoire's or Haim Gildi's. If you insist, then beat your head against a wall, but count me out of this."

As conditions got worse the arguments increased in intensity. There wasn't a moment's peace at home. Shimon's heart cried within him. He sought consolation in the words of the sages and did not find it, and when he looked into the Scriptures he inadvertently turned to a page in Ecclesiastes and his eye caught the verse, "For man does not know . . ." Man does not know his fate and is caught like a fish in a net, or a bird in a trap; like them man is beset by evil which descends on him suddenly. But why should Father and Mother be caught in such a trap—this he could not understand. But he did know from the *Gemora* that "When there is no more barley in the jug, quarrels begin in the home."

Suddenly Mother became silent and succumbed to melancholia. She did not shout and avoided quarrels. Her face underwent a change and was covered with yellowish spots. She lost her appetite, and her body, usually small, appeared

164

to shrivel. Shimon noticed once how in the midst of her work she suddenly dashed to the corner where the slop pail stood and vomited violently. He began to observe her closely and saw that she would suddenly clutch at the table or a chair to keep herself from falling. "Mother is very sick," he concluded.

One Friday evening, after the meal, Shimon sat on the sofa near the oven where the night lamp burned, deeply engrossed in a book. It was warm and comfortable in that corner. Late that evening Mother came out of the bedroom and sat on the end of the sofa, her back toward the warm oven. Shimon looked at her carefully. Her face was the color of wax; her arms were like two sticks. She sat wrapped in a shawl, her legs under her, and she looked like a little girl.

"Mother, you are not well," Shimon said.

She didn't answer at once. She moistened her dry lips with her tongue and looked sternly at Shimon.

"I don't know what is the matter with me," she finally said. "It's nothing new for me to be pregnant, and I am only in the fourth month, like Gitte. But every limb in my body is as if made of wood."

"Gitte is pampered; and you work so hard," Shimon said softly. "You should go to see the doctor; he only takes a quarter for a visit."

"I saw the doctor," she sighed. "He said I should rest and eat well and not worry. How could I tell him that I have to do the work of two? Eat well and rest—fine things, no doubt. But what should I do? I gag on my own troubles. Whom should I talk to, and who will advise me? You are a big boy now. This summer you will be Bar Mitzvah. And you have studied much. Maybe you can tell me why a poor woman who already has seven children gets pregnant in the same week as her daughter. I tried hard and yet now we may have to take charity. I am sick, and the debts are over my head, and there are nine mouths to feed. What have I done to deserve this?"

Shimon felt a lump in his throat. "I don't know, Mother," he said. "All I know is that there is a Providence. I read here in *Zemach Dovid* about troubles and evil decrees and slaughter. Entire communities were wiped out; families were eradicated. But God's will is mighty. Great kingdoms disappeared without leaving a trace, yet God preserved us and did not let us be destroyed."

Mother sighed: "It's not much consolation for the families that were wiped out. Of course, God looks after us; but now that I am sick, and there isn't a cent in the house, I might as well drown myself; but the river is frozen and I'd have to chop through a yard of ice. Even drowning isn't easy for the poor."

"Mother," Shimon said with conviction, "it says in the *Gemora* that even when the sharp sword is already against one's throat one must not despair of God's mercy."

"Say it to me in the holy tongue," Mother begged. "I want to hear what it sounds like in the *Gemora*."

Shimon repeated the words for her. She sighed, "It is good to hear words of comfort from the Torah, and when the words are read by one's own son, they are doubly precious. All the same, what will we do tomorrow right after *Havdalah*?"

"Know what, Mother? Sunday I will go with Father to work in the villages."

"What?" Mother sat up rigidly from her reclining position. "You want to be a shoemaker?"

"And what if a shoemaker? One of the *tannaim* was a shoemaker."

"I don't know how a shoemaker could become a *tanna*," Mother said. "When does a shoemaker have the time to study and become a *tanna*? Anyway, I don't know what happened long ago, but in our time a shoemaker can't become a *tanna*. And now you want to leave your studies."

"I won't give up my studies. Let me help Father at least until you get well. I'll earn something, even if not much."

"I am afraid," Mother whispered wrapping the shawl

166

tightly about herself. "You may remain a shoemaker. Too many shoemakers in the family already. It's not only the poorest paid work, it's also the lowest."

"Why is shoemaking worse than other trades!" Shimon asked.

"You're still a child, and you don't understand. People are what their trades make them. A shoemaker deals with feet, so he is the lowest of the low. A tailor makes garments, so he is a little higher. A storekeeper deals with goods that come from all over the world, so he is higher than a tailor. A rabbi deals with God who is in heaven, so he is highest of all. If you start working at shoemaking, be careful; first thing you know, all you will have on your mind will be soles and leggings—higher than that your mind won't go."

"But Mother," Shimon argued, "there is someone still lower than a shoemaker—the man who has to take charity. Don't be afraid. I won't remain a shoemaker forever. Let me go with Father into the villages, and don't start quarrels about it."

Mother sobbed quietly. Small, shriveled, her face waxen, she looked somehow shrunken. She wiped away her tears with her fists. Shimon felt the tears welling up in his eyes, but was ashamed to cry. It wasn't fitting for a boy who consoled his mother with the sayings of the ancient sages to burst into tears.

23. *Three Weeks a Shoemaker*

When, after *Havdalah,* Mother informed Father of Shimon's decision, he refused to believe his ears. "You want your son to be a shoemaker," she said curtly, "well, take Shimon with you tomorrow."

Father looked at her suspiciously. "A new stunt of yours?" he asked. But Mother looked spent and exhausted. "Let me be," she said wearily. "I have no strength left for stunts. For years you've wanted to have an apprentice. So take him with you."

"And what does he say, the scholar?"

"I am willing, Father," Shimon assented.

Father was confused. What was going on? The promising student wanted to become a shoemaker and his ambitious mother was goading him on. He was glad and resentful at the same time. He was glad because with such an assistant he could open a shoemaker's shop of his own after *Pesah,* and get rid of the bakery and all its troubles. But he also felt a twinge of regret, and a vague suspicion passed through his mind. For one thing, the arrangement came somehow too easily—just like that, without any more arguments on his part—mother and son consented. But he regretted too, that Shimon was to be his first apprentice. Mehre did not know it, but secretly Father was proud of Shimon's accomplishments. And now, suddenly, the boy's career as a scholar was to come to an end. When in the past he argued with Mehre that Shimon should help him, he did so more for argument's sake, in order to contradict his wife, without really wanting to win the argument. Now he won his point, just like that, and he wondered how he could reverse the unexpected victory. But this thought made him angry with himself. "This is what you wanted," he scolded himself mentally. "For the first time in your life you have your way." And he summoned his courage and announced cheerfully:

"Right away I will run to Elenke Rimer and get everything ready for tomorrow: raw hide and soles, a supply for five weeks. Now I will really be able to get going."

Mother said nothing and only sighed meaningfully. She was resentful. "Just look at him," she thought. "He doesn't seem to care at all that he takes the boy away from his studies. How he leaped at my suggestion, woe is me."

But she was too tired and sick and spent to voice her thoughts. She didn't even have the will to argue and remain in the right.

The following morning father and son went to a village. It was a bright and frosty Sunday morning. The road led through pine woods. The sky was a chilly blue; the snow glistened and sang under foot. Father and son carried tightly laced packs on their backs. In addition to the shoemakers' supplies and equipment, Shimon also carried in his pack a *siddur*, *Mishnaios* in one volume, and some other religious works.

They walked some miles without halting. Father was cheerful and gay and led the way; Shimon followed him. Gradually the boy became infected with his father's cheerful mood. When he left the house, he was depressed and angry with himself for having agreed to work as a shoemaker. He didn't really want to be one, and he was determined not to remain in the trade. He was angry with himself for having deceived his father. He also worried about leaving Mother behind in her state of illness, and

169

he knew that she would grieve at his going to the village. She must be crying now, he thought.

But the mood of depression dissipated as he walked in the bright morning sun on the snow-covered road that wound among the pines. Suddenly Father stopped and Shimon halted too. Father hummed a tune from the liturgy and, leaning against the trunk of a tree, he pulled the boots off his feet and slung them over his shoulder. Barefoot he again took to the road.

Shimon stared at him in amazement. "Barefoot? In the snow?" he exclaimed. But Father did not answer. A smile played under his hoar-covered moustache for a moment, and then, in a loud voice, he began to intone a melody from the prayers. When he finished, he explained to Shimon: "It's nice when the feet get good and cold, half frozen, then I put on my boots again, and my feet warm up and feel much better than before."

Shimon looked at his father and barely recognized him. He seemed to be a different man altogether. What had happened to the poor, cowering shoemaker who trembled before his wife? He now saw a transformed and proud man marching cheerily with bare feet in the snow. In his new dignity Father reminded him of Reb Getzel among his books.

Shimon did his work thoroughly. It was no great trick for him to learn the work. Father showed him once how to stretch a piece of raw hide over a board, nail it all around, and make a legging out of it. Shimon quickly learned how to sharpen the shoemaker's knife, trim a sole and scrape it with sandpaper. By the end of the first week Shimon could nail a sole and polish it with a hot iron so that it shone like a mirror.

Still, Shimon felt that Father was not satisfied with him. Father sat on a stool next to him, apparently engrossed in his work. Shimon was busy waxing a thread. He applied himself to his work diligently and all seemed to go well, but he felt Father's disapproving eyes on his back.

Late that evening he discovered the reason for Father's disapproval. They were eating their dinner. Father took baked potatoes and hard boiled eggs from the oven, and Shimon brought cold milk which the peasant woman had milked directly into a kosher pitcher. Waiting for the potatoes to cool, Shimon was busy with a book. Father talked as he ate:

"You were careful that the blacking from the thread shouldn't stick to your fingers, and after soaking the raw hide you washed your hands. Before eating you scrubbed your hands with soap so that it was positively disgusting to watch."

Shimon raised his eyes from his book. "The blacking gets into the skin," he said, "unless it is washed off at once."

"A shoemaker has to have black hands or he is no shoemaker," Father said. "Have you ever seen a shoemaker whose nails weren't black?"

"I don't know yet if I want to remain a shoemaker, so why should I get my hands permanently black?"

"In that case why do you work so hard? Why did you wax the thread so energetically if you are only passing the time?"

"When one does a job it has to be done properly," Shimon explained without removing his eyes from his book.

"You talk like a born shoemaker," Father said gleefully.

"That's not my idea," Shimon replied. "The *Gemora* says so: 'A good man may be trusted not to do an improper job.'"

"The *Gemora*, always the *Gemora*," Father muttered.

Father and son finished their supper without another word.

The peasant hut in which father and son worked was

171

lit by a torch. As late as Father worked in the evening he had a number-eight kerosene lamp, but after he finished the lamp would be put out and thin, dry sticks were inserted in the metal frame hanging from the ceiling and lit. When this kindling was well dried out it gave a fair amount of light, and the smoke would float out through an opening in the ceiling directly above. It was Shimon's job to prepare enough kindling to last the entire evening.

It was eleven o'clock at night and Shimon was immersed in his *Mishnaios*. In this peasant hut where a light burned before an image he studied the tractate *Avoda Zara* (Idolatry). But Peter, the owner of the hut, was not the kind of idolater who could be suspected of the crimes to which the ancient idol worshipers were addicted. He was most scrupulously honest and refused to take compensation for the food which Father and Shimon ate. His wife shook her head disapprovingly and chided Father: "If you want to eat dry food only, that's your business; but the boy, he's still a child, what harm would it do him to eat a plate of cabbage soup with pork fat?"

The thought of cabbage soup with pork fat made Shimon nauseous. Still, he could not associate these kind peasants with the idolaters of old. The Mishna said that a midwife must not help an idol worshiping woman when she is in labor. That is the law. But somehow Shimon was sure that Yentel the town midwife would not stand by idle even if a genuine idol worshiper needed her help. She would probably say: "Who can stand by and see God's creature suffer without helping!"

The hut was quiet. Shimon sat near the torch. Peter lay on the brick oven. His wife was busy with her spinning wheel. Father sat on the edge of his bunk reciting Psalms. Suddenly Peter came down from the oven and stopped behind Shimon.

"Yerucham, come here," he called to Father. "Tell me what kind of books are these that your boy reads all the time."

172

"These aren't books," Father told him. "These are sacred writings in the holy tongue."

"Sacred writings did you say?" Peter scratched his beard uncomprehendingly. "In the holy tongue? Come here, look."

Father came up. "Look here," Peter pointed at the page. "In the middle are little words, but on the sides they are tiny, just like dots. Can you read this?"

"I?" Father laughed. "I couldn't read them if every letter was the size of a boot. I told you, it's in the holy tongue. You have to study a lot before you can read this."

"Tell the truth now. The boy makes as if he reads. Can he really read this?"

"Fast as lightning," Father assured him.

"In that case he can read better than the village clerk," Peter decided. "So why are you making a shoemaker of him?"

"A son should follow in the footsteps of his father."

Peter laughed. "You are a fool. If the boy is such a scholar that he can read this, he is smarter than his father. You are a greater fool than a peasant. You understand nothing. He will be a shoemaker when hair will grow here," Peter concluded pointing at his palm.

This conversation between Father and the peasant took place on Wednesday of the third week of Shimon's apprenticeship as a shoemaker. They returned home on Friday of that week and Father announced: "Here, you can have your scholar back. He won't be a shoemaker in any case."

"What's the matter?" Mother asked. "He doesn't do what you tell him? Or maybe he can't catch on to the great wisdom of making peasant boots?"

"He obeys," Father conceded angrily, "and he has a good pair of hands, a real shoemaker's hands. But he won't be a shoemaker. His mind isn't in it."

Mother smiled. "Well, so there will be one shoemaker less in the family," she announced triumphantly.

Shimon went into the kitchen to wash his hands, and Father whispered to Mother: "Mehre, we must do everything we can to keep him at his studies. It took a peasant to shame me. You think I was anxious to take him with me? But just listen to what Peter said."

Mother quietly listened to Father's recital of his conversation with Peter. "The trouble with you is," she said when Father had finished, "that you never listen to what I say."

"But how will we manage now that you are ill," Father was worried.

"God will help. I already feel better. The past week I have been doing some baking. I even sent some of the tuition to the Rebbe. He refused to take it unless you promise to drop your nonsense and never again take the boy away from his studies."

"Peter taught me my lesson. Now I understand," Father promised.

"It's been long overdue," Mother couldn't resist needling Father. "Enough talking for now. It's late, but if you hurry you may still get to the bath-house. Here is your clean underwear."

Father and Shimon went to the bath-house. Mother remained in the house which already had an air of Sabbath. She was happy.

"Thank God," she murmured. "Thank God that it ended well. Monday Shimon will return to heder."

24. *Interim*

When Shimon returned from the village he noticed that Mother had undergone a subtle change. She seemed to have regained her former self-confidence and courage, yet she was also somehow more peaceful and gentle, and ceased complaining to God.

The following Sunday morning Shimon was saying his prayers at home before dawn. He had no time to go to the synagogue with Father because he had to take the bakery goods to market as soon as it got light. He frequently glanced in the direction of the kitchen and what he saw made him happy. Mother stood before the oven and with her accustomed speed she deftly tossed the freshly rolled beigel into a pot of boiling water, quickly retrieved them with a spindle and placed them in double rows on the wooden spade which she inserted into the oven. She turned them over at the right instant, and removed them just as they began to brown. She worked with a rhythm that was familiar to Shimon and that cheered him no end. Shimon noticed that she had also gained weight. But her pregnancy did not interfere with the agility of her motions and, as usual, she talked as she worked, but now there was no bitterness in her words. She addressed Shimon:

"And now, my son," she said, "I really understand what is meant by God's providence. It means something altogether different from what I had thought. I used to think that God should take one by the hand, as one leads a child, and there were times when I thought that God should lead me as one leads a horse, first right, then left, then straight ahead. Now I realize that that would be degrading for a person. A human being doesn't need this kind of guidance. A person should have a will of his own and resist events. For a moment I had lost my strength and it seemed to be the end. I became like a chunk of wood, and I didn't even care if you became a shoemaker, or if the girls went to serve in other people's homes. I was ready to become like my relative Hannah of the poorhouse and to accept charity. But now I sin no more, and I know that it is true just as the *Teitch Humesh* says: 'Better a bitter leaf from the hand of God than sweet foods from the hands of man.'"

Mother maintained her courage all through her pregnancy. She was confident that she would bear a boy and that her daughter would give birth to a girl. When this actually came to pass and Gitte gave birth to a girl three days before Mother was confined and bore a boy, she boasted:

"I knew this is the way it would be. I do not wrong the world—after each girl I deliver a boy, and after each boy a girl. My daughter is like me. Her first child, too, had to be a girl. She is my daughter, and she lives in the same house with me, and she goes in my ways."

The boy was named Binyomin. There were no more family names to be perpetuated, so Mother picked the name of the youngest of the twelve tribes.

The young Rabbi of Stohlen was an unexpected guest at the *Briss*. When Mother heard that he was coming, she went back to bed, though she had already been up and at her work for three days. "That's all I need," she said, "that the Rabbi should find me up and about, like some peasant woman who bears her child and at once rises to prepare dinner for her husband. Among respectable Jews a woman stays in bed till after the *Briss*."

The young Rabbi of Stohlen happened to visit the town by chance and came uninvited to the *Briss*. Father honored

176

him with the role of *Sandek*. After the circumcision ritual
was over, the Rabbi drank a toast to the newborn and said
to Father:

"I remember well your father, Reb Gute, though I was
only a child when he died. He was a kind and honest man,
a man of mercy. When I was a boy I loved pranks. When
your father used to drive my father in from a trip to other
towns, I tried to pluck hairs from his horses' tails. He never
let me do it. He did not scold me. He would only say,
'Motele, have you forgotten that one must not torment
dumb beasts!' "

After the guests had a drink each and tasted the cakes
that Mother had baked herself, Reb Motele began to sing.
He stood in the middle of the dining room and sang the
gay melody that was the "theme song" of the Rabbis of
Stohlen.

The scene engraved itself on Shimon's memory and to
this day he bears in his mind the image of the young
Rabbi of Stohlen—tall, lean, with a blond beard and dark
curled earlocks, his face finely chiseled, a satin caftan cling-
ing to his body, his feet in white silk stockings and lac-
quered shoes. He stood as in a trance, his long arms outstretched, his sensitive fingers moving gently to the rhythm
of the tune, so that Shimon could not tell whether they
moved to the tune, or their motion evoked it.

Many years later Shimon was with a group of friends
who mocked the traditional Jewish garb: the caftans, the
beards and earlocks; and he recalled the image of the
Rabbi of Stohlen. "It is not the traditional Jewish garb that
is ugly," he then remonstrated with his friends. "You are
familiar only with Jews beaten and defeated by poverty.
Have you ever seen a true Jewish aristocrat, a genuine
scholar in the traditional garb?"

"You think a beard and earlocks would look good on
you?" they taunted him.

"I think they would," he said. "They would certainly
bring out the Image of God in me much more than now

177

when my face is as smooth as a planed board and my modern clothes have been machine-made to fit a manikin first. If in your childhood you had seen a Rabbi of Stohlen, not on a stage, or on some special festive occasion, but in ordinary life, you would feel otherwise. How can I describe to you the beauty of traditional Jewish garb? Ordinary language can't do it. But, come to think of it, there is a description that fits the situation. Do you remember the service of Yom Kippur which describes the High Priest as he emerged from the Holy of Holies? Here are three lines from it:

> " 'Like the image of the rainbow in the cloud,
>   Like the rose in a pleasure garden,
>   Like the shining star in the East.' "

"Oh, you are just an incurable romantic," they jeered. "You surround everything traditionally Jewish with an aroma of incense and piety. It was never really like that. It is your private image."

From the day that Shimon returned from the village, he was assigned specific jobs in the bakery. He had to knead light doughs for beigel and rolls, and also for bread if the dough was not too large. In addition he had to take a basket of the freshly baked goods to market as soon as it became light outside, and he remained there till late in the morning when he was relieved by Rochel-Leah. He would then return home, have his breakfast and go to heder.

From that period Shimon most vividly recalls the freshness of the mornings, when the houses awakened from their sleep. Outwardly houses appear to be made of logs; but Shimon became aware that they were not inanimate structures and that early in the morning they woke and came to life. He never talked about this discovery to anyone— people made fun of him as it was. There was, for instance, the case of Ahapa.

The town had about three hundred Jewish families—a population of somewhat more than two thousand. In this entire Jewish population there were no loose women. Jewish young men knew about immoral women only from the references they had encountered in the Bible or the Talmud. From time to time it did happen that an unmarried girl became pregnant by some young man, who would forthwith flee to America; and the event would be such a shock to everyone that the girl's family invariably left town. But about this time the town grew considerably, and some Jews became rich and hired peasant girls as maids. Leib Poliak had such a maid named Ahapa. It was rumored that she prostituted herself to anyone for a price; but the only male associates she was seen with were the laborers from the railroad station in whose company she was to be found every Sunday.

One Sunday morning Shimon stood in the market place with his wares. There were few customers and the place was quiet. As was his habit, Shimon kept some book with him and read it in his spare time. Suddenly he heard loud laughter. He looked up and saw Ahapa with six young men. One of them carried a basket containing some bottles of liquor, a large piece of pork fat and sausages. The group came up to Shimon. He had never seen Ahapa before and was amazed by her beauty. Her complexion was clear and a flush played on her cheeks, the youthful smoothness of her neck was set off by a string of beads, her large blue eyes were rimmed by long lashes, and her long blond hair was braided in a thick plait which hung on her breast. She had a flowered kerchief on her head, and her earrings were set with blue stones that matched her eyes.

"What shall we buy, Yefim?" she said as she looked into Shimon's basket, a finger childishly touched to her lips.

"Buy whatever you want."

"Let me see now," she talked to herself. "Beigel are good after liquor, and herring goes well with bread, and pork fat with rolls, and cheese also with beigel."

179

She ordered a quantity of each and ordered Yefim to pay. He took out a large purse tightly laced with leather thongs, but then her eye caught the sweet rolls and she ordered some of those. Yefim began to count out the silver coins. "How about some extra, for good measure?" Yefim demanded of Shimon as he counted the money. Ahapa shoved him aside playfully. "You never have enough," she scolded jestingly. "You are going to have a good time with me. Let the little Jew have something too."

The young men laughed and Yefim muttered: "A regular witch, but kindhearted."

All this time Shimon gaped and did not say a word. Mechanically he took the money and didn't even say Thank You. "This is she, the whore of whom King Solomon wrote in Proverbs," raced through his head.

A new customer came up. This time it was Moishe Gerstein, the owner of a haberdashery store who was known in town as an "enlightened" man very much at home in the Scriptures. He looked with amazement at Shimon who stared after the departing Ahapa and her six escorts as they went in the direction of the forest.

"What are you staring at?" he asked derisively. "You aren't even Bar Mitzvah yet and you already have ideas."

Shimon burst out enthusiastically: "Reb Moishe! It's just like in the Proverbs!"

Reb Moishe smiled appreciatively. "So? In what chapter?"

"Some in chapters two and six, and more in chapters seven and eight."

"Right," Reb Moishe conceded. "They may not know the Proverbs, and the evil effects of sin; but in the end, when they are drunk, they beat each other up. Well, this is part of their life here; they don't expect any hereafter. And now give me two rolls, three beigel and a loaf of bread."

Shimon finished the transaction and remained immersed in thought. "In King Solomon's time and today—the world

180

hasn't changed any. In the Proverbs it says: 'Honey drips from her lips and her speech is smoother than oil. Do not covet her beauty in your heart and do not be caught in the net of her eyelashes.'"

In King Solomon's time there were Ahapas in Jerusalem.

25. *Encounters*

Kalinkovich was a minute island of Jewish life in the midst of an ocean of Gentiles; a few steps the other side of "The Sand," the new suburb, there began an alien world.

The town was surrounded by scores of peasant villages. Every day scores of peasants came to Kalinkovich to stock up on necessities. On Sundays, holidays or Fair days, hundreds of peasants would come to town. The Jews depended on the peasants for their livelihood. The peasants depended on the Jews to supply them with their household needs and their few luxuries—boots, head gear, beads, combs, nails, needles, sickles, kerchiefs, clothes and all the other necessities of civilized existence.

But though a social island, Kalinkovich was not nearly as isolated as other towns like it, Azarich, for instance, was remote from a railroad line and even lacked a church, which, in addition to its religious functions, also served to attract peasants on Fair days. Kalinkovich had both a church and a sizable railroad station. Three trains stopped daily at Kalinkovich and about the station was gathered a compact community of skilled Gentile workers whom the Jews supplied with all their needs, excepting only pork. One third the Jewish population of the town derived its livelihood from the station; and these Jews could also speak Russian fluently.

But despite these contacts, Jews and Gentiles remained

two distinct and separate entities, living according to different concepts. They were two worlds, culturally as far apart as if they had been separated by oceans.

A big pear tree stood near the church. It was an old tree, and the only pear tree in town. Its branches soared high, and the boys could never reach the topmost ones. This tree was the meeting place of the town's boys. When they tired of playing around it, they went in gangs to "The Sand" at the edge of the woods where they often engaged in gang fights with the Gentile boys. From the pear tree they also used to go to the woods to pick berries in season or to play in the sand pits.

The church stood opposite the pear tree. Over the church door hung an image of Jesus, his face full of sorrow, his head drooping in anguish, and his hands and feet nailed to a cross. Shimon looked at the image many times; but all the information he had about Jesus was that the crucified one had been a great Jewish scholar who had become an apostate, and for this reason Jewish children did not stay in heder on Christmas Eve, so that the merit of their studying the Torah should not ease his suffering. As a child, Shimon did not know that Jesus was the founder of the Christian religion—this he learned many years later, after he came to America. Before this, he sincerely believed that Jesus was a Jewish apostate who had become a god in the pantheon of the idol worshipers, like the other "idols" whose likenesses he saw the Goyim carry on painted banners during their religious processions on New Year, on other holidays, or when they went to the river to "desecrate" its waters.

In Shimon's mind time was continuous, and ancient days merged with the present—time stretched in an unbroken line from Abraham to this day. Abraham had a son named Isaac, and Isaac had two sons named Jacob and Esau between whom the world was divided. The matter appeared very simple to Shimon—the Bible story and Rashi's commentary on it settled the matter once and for all. The Bible says: "And the children struggled within her"—that is, Rebecca. Rashi asks: How could the still unborn children struggle within her? But the term "struggling" is derived from the word "running" (in Hebrew), for whenever Rebecca passed a house of study, Jacob tried to escape from her womb, and whenever she went by a temple for idols, Esau tried to run out.

When Shimon thought in this wise, the words of the Bible and the commentary automatically ran through his mind to the tune of the traditional chant: "Two peoples will come out of your womb and will go each his own way, one to evil and the other to piety, and one nation shall be more powerful than the other, and the older shall serve the younger. They shall not be equal in greatness, for when one will rise, the other will fall."

Thus Shimon had the key to understanding the world in which he lived. The present was the time of Esau's rule, and evil was in the ascendant. Jews were subject to Esau's domination and they often had to defend themselves against attack. When drunken peasants attacked Jews, Shimon was not surprised. When peasants congregated on Fair days, Jews were in danger. Shimon remembered one Yom Kippur day when Jews had to defend themselves by force. It was noon time, and the congregation was intoning its heart-rending appeals to heaven. Suddenly a number of hysterically weeping girls burst into the synagogue and said that peasants were attacking women and children outside. A wagon train had been passing through town and the peasant drivers wanted to buy food. When they found the market place deserted, they began smashing windows in Jewish homes and assaulting such women and children as they found, since all the men were in the synagogues.

Despite the solemnity of the moment, everyone doffed his *tallis* and rushed outside and, breaking the nearest fence, they seized posts and boards and rushed to the market place and dispersed the raging peasants. Then they returned to the synagogue and resumed their prayers. "And

184

all shall come to serve Thee," they intoned, and the words
of this hymn acquired new meaning for Shimon. "And all
shall come to serve Thee, and praise Thy great name, and
recount Thy justice among the nations that live on islands,
and the peoples that do not know Thee will seek Thee out.
They will praise Thee in all the corners of the world, and
they will ever say, 'God is great!' They will abandon their
idols, and be ashamed of their graven images, and bow
their backs to serve Thee."

When that day came, Shimon knew, peasants would no
longer assault Jews on Yom Kippur day; everyone would
serve the same God, and pray in synagogues.

Shimon lived in the heart of the Jewish hinterland and
he did not know that besides the peasants whom he saw
in the market place there was a world of Gentile wealth
and power and government. He encountered this world for
the first time when he was going on twelve, and this en-
counter only confirmed him in the conviction that this alien
world consisted of people lacking in intelligence. Outwardly this world appeared to him in the image of men
dressed in gaudy uniforms and highly polished boots, wearing sabres with gilded scabbards, whose heads were filled
with suspicion, wickedness and foolishness.

Shimon's older brother, Simcha, had to appear before
the authorities for a visual estimate of his age in order to
determine when he would have to report for examination
for military service. Shimon had to appear together with
Simcha, for on the estimate of Shimon's age depended
whether Simcha, who was his senior by seven years, might
be entitled to certain deferment privileges.

For this occasion Mother prepared for Shimon a new
suit. The jacket had a stiff collar, as was the custom with
such adult garb, and Mother admired the impression
Shimon made in his new garb. "He looks like a king," she
boasted. "Now everyone can see that he is a '*Gemora* boy.'
Now he looks his age."

The entire procedure appeared absurd to Shimon. Dressed in his new suit, he had to go to Mozir to have his photograph taken, then he and Simcha, their photographs safely in their possession, had to go to Dudich to have the district clerk certify their pictures, as well as their residence in the Kalinkovich municipality. Once the appropriate documents had been signed by the clerk and stamped with a wax seal, they had to report before Pesah at the county seat to appear before the examining commission.

Simcha, Shimon and a score of other young men stood in line along the wall of a large hall. They patiently waited for their name to be called in alphabetical order, and then they approached a long table behind which the examining commission sat. Simcha and Shimon were among the last to be called. The two brothers went up to the table. The officials were dressed in brilliant uniforms with shoulder boards. Swords hung at their sides, and they sat comfortably in soft chairs. Two policemen flanked the table. A clerk sat at a small table nearby.

The four gaudy officials examined the photographs of the brothers. The highest ranking among the officials at once declared Simcha to be twenty years old. His colleagues nodded assent. But when they came to estimate Shimon's age, there was general disagreement.

Shimon stood erect, his hands behind his back, and wondered why they looked at him so long. "Fifteen," the ranking official declared. One of his colleagues shook his head. "He is so small," he said. "He doesn't look more than eleven and a half to me." The third official had still another opinion. "He is small," he said, "but he is not as young as his size would indicate. Thirteen, or a little over, in my estimation." "Let's make it fourteen," the last of the group said.

At first Shimon was surprised. "How could such gaudily dressed people make such mistakes?" he wondered. As he listened to them argue, he waved his hand in disgust and muttered: "Nonsense!"

He must have spoken too loudly for the ranking official jumped up in a rage and screamed: "What? What did you say?"

Shimon was terrified and stood pale and speechless for a moment.

"Speak up! What did you say?" the official thundered.

Shimon's fear gave way to anger, and speaking a broken peasant dialect he retorted: "I said it's all nonsense! How can I be fifteen, or fourteen or even thirteen when I still don't put on *tefillin*."

He did not know the Russian word for *tefillin*. He halted a second, and then simply used the Jewish word.

"What's he babbling?" the ranking official became still further enraged. One of his colleagues, of a more even temper, asked calmly: "What does *tefillin* mean?"

But Shimon was at a loss how to explain what *tefillin* meant. A young man with a thick shock of hair moved out from his place in the line and said something in a low voice. He was called up to the table and he explained to the officials what *tefillin* were. The official said something in Russian and pointed at Shimon.

"He says perhaps you don't put on *tefillin* intentionally, so that you could claim to be younger than you are, and assure your brother deferment privileges," the young man interpreted the official's remarks to Shimon.

Shimon was amazed. "Tell him," he said to the young man, "that no Jew would do a thing like that. *Tefillin* are more important than deferment privileges. Doesn't he understand what it means not to put on *tefillin* after one is thirteen?"

The young man translated Shimon's reply to the commission and it evoked a ripple of laughter. Then they resumed their guessing game.

"Sixteen," said the first official. "He's too smart to be younger than that."

187

"Twelve," the second official proclaimed. "He is only a bright boy with a talmudic head."

"Fifteen," the third one announced.

"Let's not bother with him any more," the fourth one said. "Let's make it fourteen and a half and satisfy everybody."

"Fourteen and a half it is," they all agreed.

Shimon angrily turned to the young man who acted as interpreter. "Tell them it's an unfair judgment," he said. "I am only eleven and a half years old."

The young man repeated Shimon's words in all seriousness.

"Get out!" the ranking official ordered them.

The two policemen ran up and led them away.

When Shimon was outside, Simcha raged at him: "You babbler. You almost brought misfortune on me. Even that anti-Semite didn't give you more than fifteen years and I could have my deferment rights, so you had to open your big mouth and he wanted to put you down for sixteen."

"Is it my fault that they are such fools?" Shimon argued. "How could I be still when they were so wrong?"

"A kid like you, arguing with three officials," Simcha jeered. "You always have to try to put others in the wrong. If you had shut up, they would have put you down as thirteen, and now you will be called for the draft before you are even eighteen."

"Who knows what will be seven years from now," Shimon mused. "Maybe this too is for the good, as Nochum Ish-Gamzu said."

"There he goes again with his *Gemora* sayings," Simcha gave up in despair.

At this point the young man who had served as interpreter came out of the hall and, seeing the two brothers, he ran up to them, brimming with enthusiasm. "You sure gave it to them," he slapped Shimon's back approvingly. "How did you ever get to be so daring? And you still a heder boy, not a revolutionist. If only everybody in Russia would stand up like this to the bureaucrats!"

"What would happen then?" Shimon asked innocently.

"Tell me, are you really only eleven and a half years old?" the young man asked.

At this point Simcha could not restrain himself. "Yes, he's only eleven and a half, but he has a big mouth," he said.

"Better a big mouth and end up in Siberia or on the scaffold, than submit meekly to the bureaucrats," the young man declared sententiously and walked away.

"What's a scaffold?" Shimon asked his brother.

"A scaffold? I don't know," Simcha admitted. "But I'll bet it's nothing good. Must be a punishment of some sort."

All his life Shimon wondered about the strange consequences of the events of that day. Was it Providence that guided his tongue, or accidental childish naïveté that caused him to speak to the officials as he did? Had they estimated his age one year younger, he would have been trapped in Russia at the outbreak of the First World War, for he came to America in 1913 when he fled to avoid military service.

Who knows the ways of Providence!

On one other occasion Shimon encountered the outside world before he was Bar Mitzvah.

It was a mild, sunny Friday afternoon early in the summer. Shimon sat on the steps leading from the corridor to the garden reviewing the weekly portion of the Bible in the traditional chant. It took him a considerable time to read the portion, for he frequently stopped to consult various commentaries. Suddenly he became aware that a young man dressed in a student's uniform stopped on the other side of the fence and looked with interest at the strawberry vines that densely covered the ground in the garden.

"To whom do these vines belong, boy?" he finally asked Shimon.

"To my brother and me," Shimon answered, putting away his Bible and going up to him.

"I am a student of agronomy," the young man introduced himself. "Tell me, where did you get these vines? Did you have berries last year?"

In broken Russian, Shimon told him how two years earlier Simcha and he had found some wild strawberry vines in the forest and planted a few of them in the garden. The first year they had a plentiful harvest and picked many bowlfuls of berries. But this year, he concluded, the vines multiplied so they covered the entire ground and there was hardly a berry to be found.

"May I come in?" the agronomy student asked when Shimon finished his recital.

"Why not," Shimon invited him.

The student jumped over the fence and began puttering around the vines. For some time he examined them carefully, then he pulled a couple of vines out of the ground, carefully shook the soil from their roots, and wrapped them in a sheet of paper. Shimon watched his doings without comprehending what interested him so about such a simple thing as strawberry vines.

When he finished, the young man asked Shimon to bring him a jug of water to wash his hands with. He brushed himself carefully and explained to the mystified boy: "These few berries that I found are much bigger than the average wild strawberries, and juicier, too. Even the leaves are not the same. But the vines are too thick and choke each other, and that is why you had hardly any berries this year." He took a pencil from his pocket and a piece of paper and quickly sketched the scheme of the plant's growth. Shimon watched him with open mouth. "See?" the student explained further, "every root sends out suckers, like fingers, and they develop a root system of their own, and send out suckers in turn. If you don't thin them,

190

your garden will get choked with vines. Do you have a knife and shears?"

Shimon brought him the desired tools and both applied themselves to thinning out the dense growth. They worked for about two hours, and when they finished, perspiring and exhausted, the garden was unrecognizable. Just then Mother returned from the market place. Seeing the uniformed student she was frightened at first, but when Shimon told her what had happened, she invited him to partake of some buttermilk and beigel. The young man accepted the proferred hospitality, and Shimon resumed reviewing the weekly portion from the Bible.

"What kind of a book is that?" the student asked.

Shimon did not know how to say "Bible" in Russian, so he simply handed him the volume. The student turned to the title page and read the censor's approval that was printed in Russian. "Oh, a Bible," he said, "in the ancient tongue. In the small towns you people still waste your time on the Bible. You believe that there is a God in heaven, a God with a long Jewish beard, and that when he blows, he makes a wind, and when he sneezes it rains, and at night he spreads a sieve over the sky and the dew falls. You are a clever boy, and you have capable hands; a boy like you shouldn't stick to all this nonsense. It is time you learned about the forces of nature and the chemistry of the soil."

The student spoke Russian, and Shimon had to admit that he could not follow him. The student remarked that it was time Shimon learned Russian, if he was to learn the truth about the world.

The young man went away and Shimon returned to his reading. "And should you abandon my laws and your souls should reject my commandments . . . ," he read. The words of the student now appeared to him as an attempt to seduce him from the law and the commandments.

The following Sunday, Shimon learned that the student

had remained in town over the weekend and that he had talked also to other boys. He was of that new company that dedicated itself to enlightening the people.

In Reb Getzel's heder, Shimon was questioned closely by the older boys. "Did he really work together with you in the garden? Did he make a drawing of the plant? He talked about dew and rain? He said there is no God? And what did you say? Did he cross himself before he ate?"

Shimon was confused by all these questions. Why were they making such a fuss over a Goy who does not believe in God? And was it anything new that there were unbelievers in the world?

But the older boys were deeply impressed. The agronomy student, they felt, was one of the sages of the world. He knew the mysteries of creation. A whole week they argued heatedly about Providence, and the creation of the world, whether dew, rain, and wind came from God or were mere manifestations of natural processes.

Reb Getzel was in the habit of strolling with his pupils on "The Sand" on summer Saturday afternoons. At the time, Shimon did not realize that these walks were not taken for the sake of exercise, and that they were part of Reb Getzel's pedagogical technique. Shimon was the youngest of the pupils to be taken on these walks. The chief speakers during these strolls were Ephraim-Dovid and Avrom-Moishe. That Saturday their talk concerned the agronomy student and what he had said. It was evident that they had been deeply impressed by his declarations. Reb Getzel laughed.

"I know what goes on in my heder," he said. "Even when I am not around, I can guess what you talk about. I know your arguments by heart. A bit of Goyish wisdom reached you, and now you are all mixed up. It says in the Midrash: 'Should anyone tell you there is wisdom among the nations, believe him; but should anyone say there is Torah among them, do not believe it.' This is a profound matter. One must understand the difference between wisdom and

Torah. Wisdom teaches us 'how'—how a tree grows, how rain falls. Torah teaches us 'why.' Why was the world created? What is the purpose of the creation? What should man do to deserve bearing the image of God? Once you understand this difference, you will also understand another Midrash which states that the Torah is a draught of life for Jews, but poisonous drink for other peoples. How are we to understand this? Does the Midrash mean to say that if Goyim study the Torah they will die? Not at all; but should the peoples of the world accept the Torah, they would cease being Goyim and become Jews."

Ephraim-Dovid objected: "But Rabbi, the Scriptures are not scientific. Science makes the world more comprehensible. Nowhere in the Torah are we told how nature works."

Reb Getzel was not impressed. "No," he said. "The Scriptures don't tell us how to build a house, or how to make a pair of trousers, or how to print books. The Torah doesn't deal with such matters. All creation is subject to man. Man is the summit of creation and everything in the world was created for his sake. A good householder must know what goes on in his house. But you, no sooner do you discover how to open a door in the house, and you catch a glimpse of what is on the other side of the door, then you at once conclude that there is no God. Often when I hear you talk it seems to me that you believe that the world began with you and that everything that preceded you was chaos and without purpose, and then you came and discovered the truth."

Now, forty years later, Ephraim-Dovid says to Shimon: "Reb Getzel was indeed a scholar, that is true, but don't set him up as the source of all wisdom. I remember that stroll, but you had to remind me what he said. Somehow your recollection of what he said sounds too wise. It is what he said and at the same time it is not what he said. Were I to repeat his words, they would sound flat and provincial."

"So who is right, you or I?" Shimon wants to know.

Ephraim-Dovid waves his hand. "The very fact," he says, "that you remember what he said while I have to be reminded indicates that you heard his words not as I did. Have it your way. The quality of a melody depends largely on how it is sung. The way you sing it sounds fine. Very well, let us say that that is the way Reb Getzel also sang it. But it seems to me that the melody is strictly your own, even though the words might be Reb Getzel's."

26. *Saviors and Messiahs*

A great restlessness seized the town. Late in the afternoons, between *Minhah* and *Maariv* the synagogue was virtually deserted, but the market place was crowded with young strollers. Friday evenings and Saturday afternoons the woods near town were filled with groups of young people who talked, argued and sang. One of the woods especially was the scene of numerous meetings where local speakers and agitators from other cities harangued their audiences.

Many of Reb Getzel's pupils were swept off their feet by the new societies that sprang up in town, and a still greater number began studying Russian and discarded the traditional Jewish garb. The modern Jewish garb resembled that of the workers at the railway station. The young men wore black, blue or red shirts tied around the waist with finely woven fringed belts. The trousers were mostly of blue or green material and fitted tightly, and rubber bands passing from the cuffs under the shoes kept them stretched taut and gave them a military appearance. Their caps had shiny visors and sat jauntily on the long hair, giving them a dashing appearance. Almost invariably the young people carried Russian, Hebrew or Yiddish books.

But Shimon remained engrossed in his *Gemora, Mishnaios*, Scriptures, Midrash and moralistic works. As before, he studied diligently, untempted by the new spirit that descended on the town.

Until the age of seventeen, Shimon was not assailed by doubts. Questions did arise in his mind; but questions could always be answered, if only one sought the answer hard enough. The Torah contained all the answers; there was this difficulty, however, that the Torah was as broad as the ocean and it was not always easy to find in it what one sought.

Shimon left his father's world of artisans and entered the world of Torah scholars. He was content in this world and did not wish to leave it for another. Its discipline did not weigh as heavily on him as it did on his friends. He did not want to escape it, and saw no reason for wanting to do so. He did not feel constricted. The Torah provided him with a key to all problems. Only after Shimon reached the age of seventeen did doubts arise in his mind, doubts of a kind that were not resolved until he reached middle age. But that came later. When Shimon tries to reconstruct his state of mind at that time, he recalls the incident of the berry picking.

One Friday afternoon in late summer he went with his friends to pick berries in the forest. They went deep into the woods and scattered among the trees. Shimon found a place that abounded in berries, and in addition it was near a clearing that was almost covered with edible mushrooms. He was quite satisfied, and was about to call some of the other boys to help him weave a basket for the mushrooms when he heard Israel-Moishe calling him: "Come here, I found some bushes that are just covered with berries as big as cherries. You don't even have to pick them; you just shake them right into the dish. Come here."

"I have enough right here," Shimon answered. "Why go look some place else?"

"You won't have to look for anything, they're all around you here."

"The same here, and mushrooms, too."

"Who wants mushrooms! We came for berries."

196

"There are plenty of berries right where I am," Shimon said.

"You'll be sorry if you don't come."

Shimon didn't answer and remained where he was, and he recalls that he filled his dish with berries ahead of the others, and also filled an improvised basket with mushrooms.

This was his trait—he never abandoned his corner lightly. He never changed his ideas to conform with prevailing fashion. An idea had to grow and ripen within him before it became part of him. When he was a boy he was often called "stubborn" on account of this trait. When he grew up he was accused of being dogmatic, reactionary and old fashioned.

When this period revives in Shimon's memory, he recalls an entire gallery of would-be world saviors and redeemers. There was Goldowski, a tall, well-built young man, fair haired and always well groomed. He wore gold pince-nez and was a leader in the Bund. And Chaike-Chiene's, a slight girl with hair trimmed short, a small, thin-lipped mouth, heavy eyelashes and nervous hands. She was district agitator for the Bund. Then there was asthmatic Beinush, an old bachelor who suffered from yellow jaundice. He was a bookworm and knew almost by heart all the books that promised man a new world. A contrast to him was Shimon, the son of David-Arieh, a young man with a dense mass of reddish, unruly hair, blue eyes and a constant smile on his face. He was commander of the Bund "battle unit" in the county seat, Mozir. He always carried a pistol. Yoseph-Haim Doroshkin, whose legs were paralyzed and whose arms were like sticks, was an exception among the afore-mentioned saviors, for he was a Zionist and a Hebrew writer. He carried on an extensive correspondence with personages throughout the world. The magnate Brodsky was his patron and supported him. Doroshkin was the first Hebraist in town who on principle spoke only Hebrew to

197

those who understood the language. To this list should be added Yude the Saint, Chaike's brother-in-law, who abandoned his family and spent his days and his nights in the synagogue wrapped in his *tallis*. Six times daily he went to the *mikveh* to perform his ablutions, and he washed his hands uncounted times each day. He engaged in practical Cabala and in this manner tried to hasten the coming of the Messiah. Women believed he was a secret saint, but the men in town thought he was a simpleton.

In addition to these there was Haim Dreizhes, a hunchbacked tailor whom Shimon remembers seeing only once when he ran through the market place shouting: "Good news for Jews! Good news for Jews! A Constitution! The King gave a Constitution!" After the first elation over the new constitution came the terror of pogroms, but in between Shimon recalls the "Ceremony," an incident which introduced him to this alien word and which was attended by fear and the intimation that the new era also brought evil in its train. It came about in this wise.

Isroel-Itche became engaged to Nehama, and the wedding was set for the night of *Shabbos Nahmu*—the Saturday succeeding the fast-day of Tisha b'Av. Neither bride nor groom came from a prominent family, and the pending event did not attract much attention. The young couple worked in Mozir, the nearest large town which boasted a match factory. They pursued their employment the entire week preceding the wedding and returned to Kalinkovich as usual on Friday afternoon. Later that evening many unexpected guests began to arrive. They continued coming on foot all that night and the following day. These were strange guests—none of them was related to the bride or groom and all were very young. They wore the garb customary among the "enlightened" young people: red blouses and narrow skirts for the girls, and shirts tied around the waist with woven belts for the young men. The girls' hair was combed back and tied with red ribbon. The young men

198

all carried weapons of a kind: iron rods or wooden walking sticks with loaded knobs.

They kept the town in turmoil all that day and night. They "occupied" the woods around town where they held meetings attended by stormy debates. Ephraim-Dovid, the town's prodigy who was always informed about everything, related in the synagogue that the speakers at these meetings displayed great erudition in the writings of the new lawgivers, and lightly tossed about quotations from their authorities with the same ease that their fathers quoted the *Gemora* and its commentaries. The young men and women gathered for the wedding understood their speakers no better than the town's worthies understood the Rabbi's sermons, he reported. But they had an original custom—they applauded and shouted "Bravo" when their speaker held forth, and left the cheering to their opponents when the latter's spokesman addressed the audience.

All that Saturday the crowd of young people had the town in an uproar, and in the evening they at first monopolized the wedding, too, with their newfangled, big city dances, and their new songs which had not before been heard in Kalinkovich. But after the bride's head was covered, the relatives took over. The bride's parents led her to the canopy. It was some distance from her home to the synagogue. As usual the musicians led the parade, followed by the bride together with her parents and near relatives. After them came the crowd of local people who invariably congregated at a wedding. The groom was led to the canopy with similar pomp. Strangely, while these two parades took place, the young people from out of town were nowhere around.

The wedding itself followed traditional forms. The canopy was circled seven times, and the "Sanctification" was performed by Reb Moishe the *shohet*. Then the young guests returned and formed a crowd of their own on one side. As soon as the last of the blessings was finished by Reb Moishe, the young guests formed a circle around the canopy. A young man with long hair and wearing a red shirt climbed on a chair and began to orate. The crowd stayed to listen to him, some out of curiosity, others fearfully. The young man thundered: "The musty ceremony which was here performed by a representative of clericalism in his greasy caftan is not what has united the couple." (Reb Moishe the *shohet* was always immaculate in his dress.) "No," the young orator continued, "it is not the blessings muttered in a dead language that joined groom and bride. The true ceremony which made them one was the love which they plighted to each other. But a still higher ceremony united them, this is their oath of eternal fealty to the proletariat which, when it comes to power, will do away with all silly ceremonies such as we have witnessed tonight. We, your fellow workers, came to your wedding to swear loyalty to the proletariat. Down with autocracy! Down with all ceremonies! Long live the Bund of Poland, Russia and Lithuania!"

He jumped off the chair and the quiet summer night resounded to a volley from ten pistols.

The crowd broke through the chain of arms and fled. The canopy toppled as its bearers ran away. The bride's mother fainted, and the groom's father burst into tears for shame.

The young couple was nicknamed "The Ceremony." In Shimon's mind this term became associated with audacity, pistol shots, and the tears of a man with a gray beard.

Beinush the asthmatic was the son of Matle the widow. He was the only old bachelor in town. It was difficult to estimate his age. His face was wrinkled, his hair gray and his shoulders stooped like those of an old man. His hands, too, were shriveled and covered with veins like an old man's hands. But he used to shave, and this made him look young. When, in addition, he put a cap on his head at a rakish angle and wrapped a blue scarf around his neck, he looked not a day older than forty. His voice was

200

soft and gentle, and this too, made him seem younger than his true age.

In his youth Beinush spent considerable time abroad and studied in universities in Germany, France and England— at least that was what town rumor said. When he came back he was a sick man. He returned ostensibly to die, but he continued living for more than thirty years in his mother's house. She provided all his needs and pampered him and he, in turn, helped her with her chicken business on occasion. The rest of the time he spent reading and talking about the new and better times that were in store for humanity.

Beinush was a socialist and a Marxist, but he belonged to no party. He agitated in favor of education, enlightenment, and the just life without exploiters and exploited. When his audiences failed to understand these outlandish words, he would quickly explain that an exploiter was a robber and a deceiver. When Shimon later returned from the *yeshivah* and was already familiar with the jargon of the political parties, he quickly classified Beinush as "social conscious."

Beinush never talked about the struggle of the working people. Instead he described the beautiful and happy times that would come after the revolution. Radical party spokesmen therefore never debated with him and did not consider him an opponent. As a matter of fact, they appreciated his service in conditioning the youth for socialism, and all the radical groups favored him.

On summer evenings, especially if it happened to rain, the young people from Shimon's street often congregated in the long corridor of Shimon's house. Mehre welcomed their presence there. She loved to listen to their arguments and to hear them singing, and she tolerantly overlooked the occasional flirtations between the boys and girls. Beinush, who lived across the street from Shimon, usually joined the young crowd to enlighten them. Shimon liked to be among these carefree young people. He enjoyed their gaiety and jokes, their songs and Beinush's talks. He especially recalls one drizzly mid-summer evening. The usual crowd of apprentices and young workers were there. The young men pooled their few pennies and bought beer, which they drank with a mien of audacity. The girls barely tasted the brown liquid and exclaimed that they could not understand how anyone could possibly enjoy such a bitter beverage. When they had had enough of singing, Beinush addressed them.

"Do you think," he said, "that all the revolution will do will be to depose the Czar? Get rid of the fool, and no more? Not at all. We won't make the same mistake that other revolutions made and leave everything as it was. After the first uproar when the king is overthrown, we will start the real revolution, the social revolution. And after the social revolution there will no longer be either rich or poor. The land will belong to everyone and there will be no private owners. There will be true freedom. Not only man will be free, but also the birds and the beasts. Now my mother locks her hens in the coop, which is a prison. After the revolution there will be no prisons."

"Somehow it doesn't sound likely that there will be no prisons after the social revolution," said Eisik, a shoemaker's son who was then barely sixteen years old. Many years later, after the Bolshevik revolution, he became a commissar and sent Shimon's father to prison.

"What will prisons be needed for after the revolution?" Beinush answered with passion. "Everyone will be free to do as he pleases. Street cleaners and sanitation workers will be honored for their labors. Miners will wear uniforms like generals. As soon as there will be no exploiters, man will become honest and do only good."

"In that case, who will want to be a shoemaker or a tailor? Everyone will prefer to be an engineer, or a general, or a telegraph operator," Boruch, Elinke's son and already a full-fledged shoemaker himself, declared.

Beinush coughed, caught his breath, and proceeded to

202

explain. "Do you think, perhaps, that after the social revolution a shoemaker will work from dawn to dusk as he does now under the capitalist system? Nobody will work more than two hours a day. Finished with the work, the laborer will wash, change his clothes and do whatever he likes. If he wants to be an engineer, or a doctor, or a telegraph operator, or an astronomer, he will be able to do so. If not, he can just go about with his hands in his pockets and enjoy the weather. It will be his own free time to do with as he pleases. If he wants to he will go to a theatre."

"And you mean to say that the Goyim will allow Jews to become generals and doctors and professors?"

"You are a fool," Beinush cut his questioner short. "After the social revolution there will be no Jews or Goyim. There will only be people. Everybody will be equal."

He warmed to his subject. "The chains will be taken off mankind. No more superstitions. No more fear. Man will transform the world into a paradise. Where there is a desert now, will be a fruitful land. Diseases will be done away with. In time people won't die any longer."

Mehre sighed. "Will we live to see this, Beinush? Who cares what will happen a long time from now. All I always hear is, once there was, or, some day there will be."

Beinush answered confidently: "The social revolution must come. How soon it will come depends on us. We can hasten it."

In his corner Shimon listened to the talk and thought: "Beinush isn't saying anything new. He is talking about the coming of the Messiah and what will follow. That the coming of the Messiah depends on people has already been stated in the *Gemora*: 'If mankind will merit it, I will hasten his coming; if not, then mankind will have to wait the full term.' So what new wisdom was Beinush revealing! The *Humesh* already said that the earth belonged to God, and that the Jews were God's servants, and not man's. And as for the far distant future, hadn't Amos prophesied that a time would come when the sower would follow on the heels of the harvester, and he who treads the grapes would follow close on the heels of him who bears the seeds, the hills would flow with honey and all the mountains would become plains. And Midrash Rabbah foretold still more wonderful things for the future: 'In the days of the Messiah, God will bring ten new things. The light of the sun will be strengthened and its rays will be a healing. A spring of living waters will flow from Jerusalem and its waters will heal all ailments. Trees will give their fruit every month, and their leaves will be the best medicine. All destroyed cities will be rebuilt again, even Sodom and Gomorrah. Jerusalem will be rebuilt of diamonds. Cattle and beasts will pasture together. God will gather all the cattle and beasts and insects and make a covenant with them that they should not harm one another. There will be no more weeping and mourning. There will be no more death, and neither sigh nor groan nor sound of mourning will be heard. Everybody will be happy and joyous.' Yet here was something strange. Reb Getzel often taught groups in the synagogue about the time of the Messiah. Why then didn't people become as enthusiastic about the Jewish end of time as they did about the social revolution? There must be some great difference between the two, else how account for the fire which the preachers of socialism lit in the hearts of the workers?"

Shimon found no answer to this last question until thirty years later.

Mozir and Kalinkovich were to each other like a house and a shed. Mozir was the biggest town in the county, but Kalinkovich had the advantage of a railroad station. Goods destined for Mozir had to be unloaded in the smaller town and then hauled by ox-cart a distance of ten miles. Kalinkovich also provided its bigger sister with a large number of workers for its match factory, as well as the two chief Bund agitators, Goldowski and Chaike Chiene's.

That winter there was a prolonged strike at the match factory under the leadership of Goldowski and Chaike Chiene's. The strikers won their demands, but the police searched for the two agitators. Goldowski hid in Kalinkovich in the long street, near the slaughterhouse. One moonlit night, a carriage with four policemen drove up and arrested Goldowski. Chaike remained at large, and she was as good as any two agitators.

Chaike's father was a *melamed,* and not one of the best. He was a strange man. He seldom talked, even to his pupils. Whenever he was not engaged in his teaching duties, he recited psalms in a low voice. In town he was nicknamed "The Silent."

Chaike's mother, Chiene, was the opposite of her husband. She was a self-appointed protectress of the poor, the widows and the orphans. Each Thursday morning she went from house to house with a sack on her back and collected whatever donations she could get—flour, bread, grits, or cash, whenever any was given. Friday mornings she saw to it that the poor were provided for the Sabbath. She was never idle. If there was sickness in a poor home, Chiene was called upon for assistance. She was depended upon to get a doctor and to provide the medicine, and also some chicken soup for the patient. Wherever the hand of fate struck, Chiene was on hand and ready to help.

She did not even rest on Saturdays and holidays. She read from the prayer book to those in the women's section of the synagogue who could not read themselves. She guided other women, who had lost their place in the prayerbook, to the right page. After dinner on Saturdays she read from the *Tze'ena Ur'ena* to the neighbors. Her house was always full, and everybody in town knew Aunt Chiene. She was everybody's aunt; she was the town's aunt.

Chiene had two daughters and a son. The oldest daughter married a man from out of town. Yude was his name—

Yude the shingle maker. Some ten years after their marriage, Yude went to the synagogue one morning and never again returned home. He spent his entire days in the synagogue wrapped in his *tallis* and wearing his *tefillin*, praying and reciting Psalms. He was not a scholar and it took him some years before he learned to make his way with difficulty through a page of *Mishnaios*. Then he applied himself to cabalistic works. Nobody knew whether he understood these books, but after studying them for a time, he began to fast every other day, he frequented the *mikveh*, and washed his hands innumerable times. On those days when he did not fast, he contented himself with dry bread and salt, and this he washed down with water. He never touched meat, not even on Sabbaths. Women believed that he was a *Lamed Vovnik* and was capable of performing miracles, but for the time being preferred to conceal his powers. Some day, they whispered, he would reveal his true identity and show what he could do. Whenever some misfortune struck a home—a child fell ill, or a woman had a difficult labor—they came running to Yude and begged him to help. He remained silent, as was his habit. He would merely pull the *tallis* over his face and remain thus until the women departed. But the women were not discouraged and kept imploring him for help. They called him Yude the Saint. The men, on the other hand, smiled when his name was mentioned and knowingly pointed to their foreheads—he was a simpleton, an ignoramus, and a bit wrong in the head, they hinted.

But many artisans revered Yude. Shimon's brother-in-law, Shmuel-Haim, was a great admirer of Yude, and saw to it that his clothes were always in good repair and his shoes whole. The day of each new moon Yude would come to visit Shmuel-Haim. He would come late at night when everybody was already asleep, and knock on the kitchen window. Shmuel-Haim would wait for him and open the door. On a little table in the kitchen there would stand ready a jigger of liquor, bread and salt, a hard-boiled egg, and a glass of tea.

Shimon, who slept on the sofa near the kitchen, always saw these visits. His brother-in-law would wait on Yude and never sat down in his presence. The visits followed what seemed to be a rigidly prescribed routine. Yude would wash his hands, dry them on a kitchen towel, and murmur the prescribed blessing. Then he would break off a piece of the bread, dip it in salt and say *Hamotzi,* and Shmuel-Haim piously said Amen. After this, Yude would take the jigger of liquor and say: "*Lehayim,* Reb Shmuel-Haim! May God grant a month of health and subsistence to you and to all Israel!" Then he recited the blessing prescribed for liquids. Shmuel-Haim would say Amen twice, and believed implicitly that the well being enjoyed by his family was due to Yude's blessing. This little ceremony was repeated each month.

Chiene's only son lived in Kiev where he was a Hebrew teacher, and contributed articles to Hebrew periodicals on Zionism and pedagogy. Years later Shimon met him and was strongly influenced by him.

Chiene's younger daughter was none other than Chaike. She was a temperamental girl, well read, and a devoted revolutionist. In character she resembled her mother; always ready with a retort and full of energy. She traveled from town to town organizing revolutionary groups. It was rumored in Kalinkovich that she always carried a pistol with her.

After the strike in the match factory, she went into hiding, but right after Passover a rumor spread that she would come to the First of May demonstration organized by the Bund and deliver a speech.

Shimon's brother-in-law had an apprentice named Nissel who was the secret leader of the Bund. Looking at him no one would have guessed it. Outwardly he was a gay, talkative and sociable young tailor's apprentice. It was strange, moreover, that he never talked about revolution, a very popular subject among his kind. Shimon nagged him for information on the much discussed rumor regarding Chaike's return.

"Will she come?"

"Must you know?"

"Will she make a speech?"

"Will it interfere with your study in the *Gemora* about the egg that was laid on a holiday if you don't know whether she will make a speech?"

"Why are you afraid to tell?"

"If one is afraid, he recites *Shema Yisroel*, but I, as you see for yourself, am busy stitching a jacket."

"I won't tell anyone," Shimon pleaded.

"What you don't know you are sure not to tell."

"You think I am an informer?"

"God forbid."

"So why don't you want me to know?"

Nissel bent over Shimon and whispered in a confidential tone. "You really want to know? Better go slow."

Shimon laughed and Nissel started to sing.

The first of May came, but the town remained undisturbed. The stores were open, the children went to heder, in the market place the women stood over their wares. The only sign of unrest was the presence of a few police officers who wandered around the market place.

The morning passed and still there was no sign of anything unusual in the streets. The artisans remained in their shops and the stores did their usual business. Only the children in heder were tense. They knew that in case a demonstration started they would be dismissed. Yet the sun was already setting and there was no sign of any demonstration.

Only when the sun was already low over the horizon and the children were dismissed, did the demonstrators gather on the bridge. The children dashed toward the river.

A crowd had congregated near the bridge, but access to it was barred by a human chain of workers whose arms were linked and who permitted no one to approach too close. All of them wore black shirts and red belts, and each carried an iron rod topped with a knob.

Shimon noticed Nissel inside the human chain. He pushed as close as he could and shouted to him: "Will she be here?"

"You'll get older and you'll find out," Nissel answered. "Now stand still; watch and keep quiet."

Four young men carrying two empty barrels appeared on the bridge. They rested a board on the barrels, and suddenly there was Chaike standing on the improvised platform. No one recognized her at first. She was dressed like an orthodox woman, a kerchief low over her forehead. But as soon as she removed the kerchief and shook her bobbed hair free, the crowd recognized her and a cheer went up. Nissel stood at the edge of the crowd and smiled.

Chaike started to talk. Shimon strained to catch every word, but he could not understand everything, for Chaike spoke a strange tongue. It was Yiddish, to be sure, but she used many Russian and other difficult words which he had never heard before.

She did not speak long. As soon as she finished all the demonstrants raised their right hands and shouted in unison: "Down with the Autocracy! Down with Czar Nicholas! Long live the revolution! Long live the Bund!" Then they began to sing the *Shevuo* (The Oath), and the sound of their combined voices was re-echoed from the forest. Chaike jumped off the board and began to walk in the direction of the woods. For a while her bobbed black hair could be seen as she walked through the open field, then she disappeared among the trees.

The following day the town was overrun by policemen. Many young men were arrested. They looked for Chaike, but could not find her. Nissel was left alone.

Some weeks passed and the police did not give up their

search. Shimon asked Nissel: "Will they catch her?" But Nissel only smiled: "It's not easy to recognize her."

In the end Chaike was caught. She was recognized by a police officer in a neighboring village as she went with a peasant woman to dig potatoes.

Late that night Shimon heard Yude knocking on the kitchen window. Shmuel-Haim was already asleep, but the familiar knock on the window roused him at once and he leaped out of bed to open the door. From his place on the sofa Shimon watched his brother-in-law make the usual preparations. But when Yude raised the whisky glass he departed from his usual formula. He said: "*Lehayim*, Reb Shmuel-Haim! God grant that her suffering be an atonement for her sins!"

"Whose sins, Rabbi?" Shmuel-Haim asked when Yude finished his drink.

Yude took a mouthful of bread and chewed it slowly. He thought for a while before he spoke. "I mean Chaike," he finally said, "my sister-in-law. It's a pity. I brought her up. I carried her in my arms. She always had a kind heart. And now Satan has misled her. I heard that she always carries a pistol, ready to kill. She doesn't know that 'Because you have drowned someone, you will be drowned yourself; and in the end they who drowned you will also be drowned.' It is a vicious circle, the exact reverse of the circle which a saint makes against evil."

Shmuel-Haim was confused. He had never before heard Yude talk so much, and he did not quite understand what he now heard. In the end his curiosity overcame his reverence and he asked: "Rabbi, you are blessing her?"

Yude shut his eyes and said: "I wish her that the suffering which she will endure at the hands of the wicked should atone for her sins. May she begin to do good to man, like my mother-in-law, then there will be another good person in the world."

Yude said no more. He recited grace, kissed the *mezuzah* and went his way.

Shmuel-Haim went up to Shimon's bed and asked:

"Are you asleep, Shimon?"

"No."

"Did you hear?"

"Yes."

"Do you understand what he meant?"

"I think I do."

"What did he mean by 'circle'?"

"He meant that it is an endless business. She will kill someone, and then she will be killed, and later her murderer will be killed, and so on, without end, like a circle which has no beginning and no end—the evil remains forever."

"And what did he mean by the circle that a saint makes against evil?"

"When a saint wants to overcome demons and devils and Satan, he makes a circle about himself and does not let them come close. He protects himself from them."

"I still don't understand it entirely," Shmuel-Haim said. "But I am surprised that a saint like Yude should think that one like her is a good woman."

Shimon did not answer. He recalled Beinush's speech about the social revolution which sounded like a paraphrase of the promises contained in the Scriptures and the Midrash. Now it appeared that Yude the Saint was also trying to understand the difference between the two.

27. *The Vanguard*

The Russo-Japanese war broke out, but Shimon was not impressed. To him wars were like blizzards, rain storms and other harsh natural phenomena. They would happen again and again—until the Messiah came. And Messiah would come after the greatest of all wars, the war of Gog and Magog. Nevertheless, he was not indifferent when he saw the parties of new recruits marched through town on the way to the railroad station. They were like sheep being herded to slaughter; even physically they looked like flocks of sheep, in their gray coats and sheepskin caps, their eyes blank and submissive, the pounding of their feet against the ground raising clouds of dust like those raised by a flock of sheep returning at nightfall from their pasture. Shimon watched the long ranks as they passed and was baffled. Russia, people said, was at war with Japan. Who was "Russia" that it could command these mute mobs?

In the railroad station Shimon saw a huge placard on the wall, near the image of Jesus. It showed a tall Russian soldier in rawhide boots, a sheepskin coat held firmly in place by a red belt, and a sheepskin cap. Countless minuscule Japanese swarmed all over him. The soldier laughed hilariously. The inscription on the placard read: "Careful, bugs, I'll shake once and you will all fall down!"

Shimon studied the placard and disapproved its levity. What was Ivan so gay about? War was no joke; it was

God's punishment for sins committed. And who could tell whether Russia or Japan had sinned more? And which country would be the rod of chastisement in God's hand? It was a time for repentance, Shimon concluded, and not for joking.

He recalled a passage from *Tanna Debei Eliahu:* "The Jews who sinned (in the days of the Judges) were like school children. What should be done to them? He punished them once and a second time and a third time and they repented." But the Gentiles, Shimon thought, take their punishment lightly. They have bands playing on the battlefields. Woe to the world, since the Gentiles do not know God's Torah.

The war raised havoc also in town. Sons, husbands and brothers were drafted into the army. There was much Psalm reciting on their behalf, and women ran to measure the graves as a remedy against having a near one taken for military service. To this day Shimon remembers the wailing of the women in the cemetery and the mournful tones of the Psalm sayers.

Then came the day when Jewish reservists had to appear for induction, and the town was in mourning. That evening the reservists went from house to house to collect the tax which they had levied on every household on their own authority. This led to frequent trouble. Not all householders readily contributed the sums demanded of them. The reservists, on their part, shouted:

"What? We leave wife and children without support and you begrudge us another penny?"

These arguments were not always confined to shouting. The reservists got drunk, and while intoxicated they smashed whatever came to hand.

Shimon's house was bypassed by the reservists. Some of them had served in the same regiment with Shimon's father, but they did not know that he had been given a "white ticket" (rejection papers) the last time he went for the required three weeks' training, and was therefore not subject to further call.

Father was pale and distraught. For a long time he said nothing, but in the end he could no longer control himself and said to Mehre: "We should have given them something."

"You're looking for trouble?" she retorted. "They might smash everything in the house. We have hardly a cent to our souls, and what they don't know won't hurt them. Let them think you're still a reservist. I'll contribute my share later."

Mother put out the lamp. The entire town remained awake all night and did not calm down till dawn, when a train came and took the reservists away.

Shimon knows that Father's one-man strike against war work occurred during the early months of the Russo-Japanese war, and that the turbulent discussions in the synagogue of the defeats in Manchuria and their implications for the country took place later. But when he resurrects the memory of those days, first to come to his mind is the vision of agitated groups talking heatedly and repeating such outlandish names as Kuropatkin, and Makarov, and saying such weird things as "chopping down people like cabbage." Then the other incidents. So he relates them in this order.

He recalls the Old Synagogue in the twilight hours of a Sabbath. Leiser-Itche the Enlightened (thirteen years later, under the Bolsheviks, he became the town commissar), stood in the midst of a circle of men and held forth:

"Men were chopped down like cabbages, simply chopped down. Ivan got what was coming to him. General Kuropatkin was in charge of Port Arthur. And you ought to know that Port Arthur was not just any kind of fortress. It was fortified four different ways. First there was a moat, a kind of deep ditch filled with water, more than the height of a man. After the moat came the trenches filled

214

with soldiers and guns, long barreled guns that could shoot twenty miles away. And the soldiers swarmed all over, like bees. Or do you think there aren't enough soldiers in Russia? And after the trenches, some distance away, was a stone wall, and on it were more guns. And behind the wall were towers with more guns, each manned by the best Russian gunners, and soldiers with spy glasses, scouts, who were on the lookout day and night; and every time they noticed something moving in the distance they gave a signal with flags and the guns started shooting, and every shell was big enough so it could wipe out an entire regiment.

"So there Kuropatkin was inside the fortress with nothing to do. What was there for him to do? He was protected on all sides. So he spent the time drinking and whoring. He wasn't afraid! Who would dare attack his fortress? He had plenty of guns and outnumbered the Japs ten to one.

"But the Japanese didn't sleep on the job either. They worked out a plan. They are a strange people, the Japanese. They consider their king to be a god, and when the Japanese king calls one of his generals and says to him: 'You and your regiments are dead!' they believe him and consider themselves dead."

Leiser-Itche stopped as if to catch his breath, but he really wanted the pause to let the effect of his words sink in his audience and to give them an opportunity to question him. Shimon's heart trembled with anxiety and curiosity. He would have liked to know the end of the story, and he also would have liked to ask Leiser-Itche how it was possible for the Japanese king to give such a command to his troops. He was on pins and needles, but dared not ask the question. He knew that someone would at once scold him: "Get out from under foot! Who told you you could listen in?" And he would be driven away and would never know the end of the story.

Shimon therefore forced himself to be silent. But unwittingly, Borukh-Meier the wool comber came to his assistance. Borukh-Meier was normally a taciturn man, not out of an excess of wisdom but simply because he had little to say. He was one of the very few Jews in town who could barely read his prayers and could not write at all. Nevertheless, he was held in a certain respect because of his wool combing machine.

Borukh-Meier owned a wool combing machine with which he earned his livelihood. For a long time it was believed that he had invented the machine. Later the town learned otherwise, but some of the former respect continued to cling to him; for even though he had not invented the complicated mechanism, he did know how to keep it in repair. This was no mean accomplishment, as the town learned. After many years of being the sole wool comber in town, a young man, just married, imported another wool combing machine all the way from Kharkov and set up as competitor to Borukh-Meier. For some months all went well, and then the young man's machine broke down. It took him more than a month to bring a mechanic from Kharkov. The mechanic looked at the machine and declared that a couple of rollers were broken and that they would have to be replaced. This meant a big expense. The mechanic would have had to stay in town until the rollers were brought from Kharkov, which would take at least a month, and meantime he would draw a mechanic's wage. The young man sold his machine for a trifle to Borukh-Meier, and the latter repaired it in two days.

Now Borukh-Meier stood in the circle of men and stared at Leiser-Itche. Then he spoke in short abrupt phrases, as was his habit:

"So, tell us, what do you mean 'dead'? How could he say to living people, 'You are dead'? Don't they eat and drink and do all the other things like living people? Well? How could it be?"

Leiser-Itche was obviously pleased with the question. It gave him the desired opportunity to explain the matter.

216

"Reb Borukh-Meier," he began condescendingly, "surely you know that when someone dies in our midst the *shammes* says to the corpse: 'Be informed, Itzhak ben Reb Avrom, that you are dead. Your wife is no longer your wife, and your children are no longer your children, and you no longer have anything to do with the world of the living.' Well, in Japan they do likewise. The Japanese king says to a general and his soldiers: 'Be informed that you are dead. Your parents are no longer your parents, your wives are no longer your wives, and your children are strangers to you.'"

"I don't get the sense of it," a number of voices called out at the same time.

"The sense of it is simple enough," Leiser-Itche answered in a singsong. "When the Japanese Goyim hear this command, they no longer have anything to lose. They have to fight to the death. They can't return home, and they can't allow themselves to be taken prisoners, because what would they do after the war, and how would they return home? Their only way out is to be victorious in the war, and then they are accounted alive again according to Japan's law. Well, it is hard to beat such soldiers. They go into battle without fear, hoping only for happiness after death or for return to life through victory. How is it possible to fight such soldiers? So that's how Port Arthur fell."

"But what about the moat, and the trenches, and the towers, and the long barreled cannon?" there were protests from all sides. "And what about the Cossacks, and Kuropatkin?"

"Kuropatkin?" Leiser-Itche jeered. "Nothing to him. He was a great general, but a still bigger drunk. So he forgot that there are dark winter nights. The water in the moat froze, and there was a blizzard; and the Japs, with their couple of pounds of rice in their pockets, their rifles and ten pounds of bullets crossed the moat. And once they were over the moat, what good were the trenches and the cannon that shoot twenty miles away? So from the trenches they went to the towers and then into town and they captured the general and all his cannon and soldiers and Cossacks and horses."

"Go on! And you mean ours didn't do anything? What's the matter? Ivan can't fight?"

"Who said they didn't do anything? Didn't I tell you that people were chopped down like cabbages? Ours fought and stabbed and engaged in hand-to-hand combat. People fell like flies. The snow turned red from the blood that was shed. But the Japs believed themselves dead who could only come to life in the hereafter or through victory. The battle was their sole salvation. They had nothing to lose."

Shimon heard the phrases, "chopped like cabbages," "dropped like flies," "become alive after they fall," and his brain was in a turmoil. How could the dead return to life, and the living regain their lives through victory?

One man, similarly confused, spat in disgust and declared, "It doesn't make sense." But Leiser-Itche wasn't fazed. "Tell me," he challenged the skeptic, "did Port Arthur fall or didn't it?"

"It fell," the man had to admit.

"Now tell me," Leiser-Itche persisted, "wasn't Port Arthur a mighty fortress, unequalled in the world, with many soldiers and great armament, so how could a fortress like this fall?"

"What do you mean 'How could it fall?' It was taken, with war strategy."

"That's just what I was telling you," Leiser-Itche triumphed. "Everything I told was just that—the war strategy of the Japs. Their king is a god, and his soldiers practice *Kiddush Hashem* for him."

"Say at least *lehavdil*," Yoshe the blacksmith said angrily. "Here is a new kind of *Kiddush Hashem* for you. They go to kill people and to conquer land, and he calls it *Kiddush Hashem*" (Sanctifying the name of God).

"Among Goyim," Leiser-Itche explained, "it is *Kiddush*

218

Hashem to get killed in a war. The more they are Goyim, the greater the glory of being killed in war."

"So, you mean to say," Borukh-Meier interjected, "that the Japs who go to battle with a song are even bigger Goyim than our Ivans? Go on! There are no bigger Goyim than ours."

"You're right," Leiser-Itche agreed. "When it comes to fighting there is no one like our peasants. But you know why they are catching it in Manchuria? Because the people here are at odds with the Czar. That's why the army is catching it time after time, and they will catch it still more. The people don't want to fight, and there will be defeats until the people get a constitution. Then things will improve in the country and the people will be glad to fight again."

"Happy to hear it," Seichik the grocer jeered. "The people will get a constitution and then they will be glad to fight again. You know what it means? It means that we will have first rate pogroms. When Ivan starts swinging, it's no laughing matter."

"You keep out of politics, Reb Seichik," Leiser-Itche reproved him. "Politics is not like groceries. It takes a head to understand politics."

On this note the discussion ended and the group dispersed.

Shimon recalls another discussion like the foregoing one, and again the subject was the fighting in the far-off war, but this time a naval engagement was debated. The proud Russian fleet, many ships, sailed forth against Japan. No one interfered with them. Admiral Makarov vaguely wondered at the ease of his progress. The Japanese too had a navy, so why didn't they give battle? And yet he was not surprised either. Wasn't he the mighty Russian admiral? And wasn't every Russian sailor the equal of ten Japanese? He did not realize that he was being lured into a trap. A mine field had been planted in his path. But

Makarov was lucky and the mines did not explode. He safely crossed the mine field and he met the Japanese fleet. Makarov withdrew to regroup his forces, but this time the mines did explode.

"It all sounds too easy," Yoshe the blacksmith grunted. "One-two and the Russian fleet is destroyed. Just like that! And where were the mine-sweepers? And why didn't our side plant mines? Heh? And where were all the cannon and the machine guns on the ships?"

"That's just it," Leiser-Itche triumphed. "It's just as I explained it last time. There weren't enough minesweepers and guns. Ivan, the bureaucrat, is a thief and money that should have gone for minesweepers was stolen, and the people look on and are glad; because when the Czar, the Little Father, catches it from the Japs, the real dance will start here. You just wait and see."

Leiser-Itche's political reasoning made Shimon's head swim. The entire business was incomprehensible to him. First of all, why should there be wars? Of course, there had always been wars; the Book of Kings is full of them. But those were wars of the Jews against their oppressors. Shimon knew, for instance, of the great wars in the Heights of Gilead: Aram seized a Jewish city and the Jews wanted to free themselves from the foreign yoke. But what was the present fighting all about? He was particularly disturbed by the phrase "people are chopped down like cabbages." How could one speak like this about people? He closed his eyes and tried to visualize how a sword is lifted and then descends down, down, down until it cuts into the flesh. Nights on end Shimon had feverish visions of wounded soldiers lying abandoned in the snows of Manchuria.

The war also struck close to home. Many Jewish soldiers from the town served in the army. There was much more Psalm-saying now, and the air in the cemetery was often rent with the wailing of women. Yet despite this, the town

220

seemed to take the war for granted the same way it took for granted a blizzard or a flood, or any other natural catastrophe. Only one man in the entire town rose up against the war. This was Shimon's father.

This was the first time that Shimon sided with his father. And it should be noted that whenever anyone in town failed to conform and stubbornly clung to his convictions, he would usually be branded with some nickname to describe his deviation. But no nickname was attached to Shimon's father. The town sensed his earnestness and sincerity and realized that it would be out of place to jeer at sincere conviction.

In far-off Siberia young lives were sacrificed daily by the thousands, but in the town the artisans, especially the shoemakers, had their day. The battles took place in a cold country and the troops needed clothing to suit the climate. Warm footwear was especially important and every soldier was issued felt boots, soled with thick raw leather. Army contractors came to the town and placed large orders with the local shops. Shoemakers suddenly were in great demand. Fast workers earned as much as twenty-five rubles a week, and even the slower ones earned up to eighteen rubles.

Uncle Itche had a shop employing twelve laborers. As always in the summer, Shimon's father worked for him making ready-made boots. Usually Father earned very little at this work, but when Uncle Itche contracted to deliver a large order of felt boots, Mehre had great hopes. Father was expert at this work, and the felt boots he made for the peasants during his winter visits to the villages were famous in the entire neighborhood. She now expected him to prosper.

Shimon noticed that during the week when Uncle Itche's shop began working on the government order, Mother started to pamper Father as if he were an only child. All week she talked of the fat earnings Father would bring

221

home and how she would spend them. If only the work would last a couple of months it would be possible to fix the roof and to get another cow. All week Father ate the specially prepared dishes, but his face was grim and he did not say a word. No one seemed to notice this in the excitement, only Shimon was aware that something was brewing.

Saturday evening, immediately after the prayers, Father went to collect his wages. Mother ordered Simcha to prepare the samovar, and when Father returned, the boiling samovar stood in the middle of the table surrounded with sparkling glasses on porcelain saucers. There was also a bottle of raisin wine for *havdalah*. Mother even had a dish of jam on the table.

Father came in and drily greeted the household. Shimon looked at his face and realized that there would be trouble. What could have happened? Had Uncle Itche "fired" Father? No. He wouldn't do anything like that. Then what could have happened?

Father avoided Mother's eyes. He recited the *havdalah* mechanically and without any feeling. Shimon noticed that Mother's face clouded. She, too, had become aware that something was wrong. After the *havdalah*, Father poured himself a glass of tea, but he did not touch the jam. He sipped the scalding tea, then he inserted two fingers into his vest pocket and withdrew the weekly wage—three bulky coins in a blue piece of paper that usually served as wrapping for lump sugar. This he placed on the table before Mother.

Mother unwrapped the coins, looked at them once, and stared uncomprehendingly. She placed the three heavy silver ruble coins on the palm of her hand, as if weighing them. Then she put them on the table and examined the paper wrapper, as if to make sure that she hadn't overlooked any of its contents.

"Benche, what is the meaning of this?" she asked Father, her voice strangely calm.

222

Shimon stared at Father. He saw that Father was mustering his courage. He sipped twice from the glass, then slowly put it on the saucer. Without raising his eyes Father said:

"Wages, as usual."

"What do you mean? That's all he paid you?"

Father blew on the hot glass; his voice rigidly controlled, he said briefly: "Just that; that's all he paid."

Mother lost her patience and her words burst out in a torrent. "What is he thinking of, your fine boss, the phony scholar who studies *Mishnaios* after prayers, just because he is your uncle he can pay you anything he likes? Nowadays they pay gold for soling felt boots, and just look at what you brought home."

Mother tossed the three heavy coins on the table and their ringing sound echoed through the room. Father calmly sipped his tea and did not answer. This further exasperated Mother and she began shouting angrily: "I talk to you, and you . . . Why don't you say something? Have you lost your tongue?"

Father drained his glass and banged it on the saucer. Now he, too, was angry and beside himself. "I told you," he shouted, "that he didn't give any more. Stop your nagging!" Then he poured himself another glass of tea and slurped it loudly. Mother stared at him in disbelief. As was her habit on such occasions, she folded her arms over her bosom and indulged in one of her monologues: "Somehow I fail to grasp what is going on here. All shoemakers are literally making gold, and you bring me three miserable rubles. Here I had thought that we were on easy street, that you will make big wages and we'll pay the tuition and buy some clothes. First, you need an overcoat; your old one is falling apart. And then your Sabbath suit, which used to be black, the way it should be, by now has no color at all. It's a shame to wear it even on *Tisha b'Av*. And I had thought that we'd get a different cow. And now you come with the same wages as before. Three big round rubles, and there you are! What should I do first with this treasure?"

Father regained his speech: "So, you tell me; why did you just now notice that I make three rubles a week? Isn't this what I always earn working on ready-made boots? What's the matter? I'm too lazy to work maybe?"

"I know, I know," Mother interrupted him impatiently, waving her arms. "I know you work like a slave. You always work hard and you always earn enough to buy either salt or pepper. You're a ne'er-do-well and too honest at your work. Your stitches always have to be just so, no matter what you work on. But you do know how to sole felt boots. Your peasant boots are famous for many miles. And now you get paid for soling felt boots the same as for ordinary ready-made ones. I won't let your fine uncle get away with it. I will go to him and I will ask him a single question: 'Why? Eisik the patcher, who can't make a proper pair of peasant's sandals, makes twelve rubles a week. His wife told me so herself. And my Benche who turns out first-rate work brought me three rubles.' "

"Stop throwing the rubles in my face," Father answered angrily. "You can depend on it that Uncle Itche is an honest man. He won't cheat you."

"I know, I know," Mother sneered. "All rich people are honest, until it comes to their pockets, if you let them get away with it. But I won't let it pass. God willing, this Saturday I will go to see him, and I know how to talk. I am not a ninny like you. I'll make sense of it."

Shimon did not believe his ears. Father jumped up in a rage and pounded the table.

"Don't meddle, I tell you," he shouted. "It's none of your business! Keep your woman's nose out of men's business!"

Mother half closed her eyes and her lips became rigid, as always happened when she was determined and knew her course of action. Meantime she had to dispose of Father's remark and she said ironically: "Just look at my provider rage. Just look at his manly advice. This whole business doesn't sound right to me. There is a secret here; something is being kept from me. But I don't like secrets and I insist on knowing what's going on."

Father lowered his head and toyed with his glass of tea. Neither of them said another word.

The following Saturday after the meal, when Father took his usual nap, Mehre said to Shimon: "Take your *Gemora*. We will go to Uncle Itche for a visit."

Shimon looked at her questioningly, but she only grimaced and said angrily: "My prodigy! Do I have to explain things to you too? I want that Uncle Itche should test you."

"What will he test me on? The portion of the week? But I am now studying *Pesahim* and not the weekly portion of the *Humesh*."

"I know," Mehre said wearily. "But I have a plan. Uncle Itche thinks he is a scholar, so he will feel flattered when I bring you to him that he should test you, and then it will be easier for me to talk practical matters with him."

Shimon smiled: "Mother, you've got everything figured out. Your head works all the time."

"What good is my wisdom," she said self-deprecatingly. "Wisdom without luck is like a knife without bread, like a needle without thread."

But Uncle Itche was not as flattered as Mehre had expected him to be. No sooner had Shimon finished reciting his page from the *Gemora*, and before even Aunt Rive served the refreshments, Uncle Itche said irritably:

"Listen to me, Mehre, I know you are an intelligent woman who always has a purpose. You can't fool me. So tell me why all of a sudden you brought your scholar for a test? Since when do you think of me as a scholar who can follow a dispute in the *Gemora*?"

Meantime Aunt Rive served tea with jam and cookies. Mehre calmly stirred the jam into her tea, then she smoothed the kerchief on her head. Shimon followed her every motion and wondered: How would she evade Uncle

Itche's forthright challenge? But Mehre did not lose her composure. She spoke quietly and sweetly even as she rhythmically stirred her tea:

"Uncle, may you live long and enjoy good health. You guessed right that I had a purpose in coming here. So I'll get to the point. All I want to ask is: Where is justice? And where is your Jewish heart? Why did you pay my husband three rubles a week for soling felt boots while Eisik the patcher got twelve rubles? Isn't my husband a good man with his hands?"

Uncle Itche interrupted the flow of her speech. "What is your argument? Who told you that your Yerucham soles felt boots?"

The question dazed Mother so that she stuttered: "What do you mean?"

"I mean what I said," Uncle Itche was impatient. "Who ever told you that Yerucham soles felt boots?"

Mother regained her composure. "In that case," she said harshly, "the injustice is still greater; it's outright robbery. Every no-good soles felt boots and makes a lot of money, while you keep my husband working on ready-made boots for stock."

Now Uncle Itche was calm and sifted his words through his teeth: "And who told you that I keep Yerucham at this work, that I don't let him sole felt boots?"

"Stop playing riddles with me," Mother pleaded, "and tell me outright what is going on. If you give him felt boots, why doesn't he do them?"

"Why ask me?" Uncle Itche said wearily, as if the whole subject bored him. "Ask him, ask your husband; he is closer to you. All I know is that he refuses to sole felt boots. Why? Ask him, maybe he will tell you."

Shimon followed the conversation eagerly, but he could not guess the answer. Mehre noticed an undertone of irritation in Uncle Itche's voice, and she changed her tone to a plea: "Please forgive me, Uncle, and don't take it amiss that I talked the way I did; but in what you said, and what

226

my husband said there is a mystery that I cannot unravel. He says: 'Uncle Itche pays only three rubles a week.' And you say: 'He doesn't want to sole felt boots.' So what is the truth of the matter? My heart bleeds. The children go about barefoot and in rags. I am over my head in debt. The older girl has reached marriageable age and all she has is one dress to her name, and the younger one is growing up fast. Yerucham Benche wears a suit that is falling apart. And now that all shoemakers are doing well, I thought that we, too, would see the light. And here is a fine mess—who can figure out what goes on here?"

Mother's eyes filled with tears and she wiped them with the end of her kerchief.

For some time Uncle Itche didn't say a word and stared at the design of the blue-and-white tablecloth. Then his right hand tentatively toyed with the silver teaspoon. Shimon saw that he was searching for words but could not find them at the moment. Finally he said with a sigh: "I understand how you feel, but what can I do to help you? Sigh along with you? Can I tell you everything that happened in the shop this week? I had plenty of heartache with Yerucham. But I keep on talking and he sticks to his argument: 'I don't want that people should be killed in the felt boots I make.' "

"What!" Mother rose from her chair.

"I didn't want to tell it to you before," Uncle Itche whispered.

Mother sighed deeply and again wiped her eyes. "Come, Shimon," she said. "Take the *Gemora* and let us go."

"Don't take it ill of me that I talked as I did," she said to Uncle Itche. "My heart aches, so I shout."

"I know, I know," Uncle Itche nodded understandingly. "A good Shabbos, Mehre."

"A good Shabbos, Uncle."

After dark, Mother set the samovar and the glasses and saucers on the table, and also wine for *havdalah*, and a dish

227

of jam, all as on the preceding Sabbath. When Father came in, he was surprised at the preparations. He recited the *havdalah* and then withdrew his week's wages from his vest pocket. This time Mother did not unwrap the money in the blue paper. Instead she poured a glass of tea and stirred some jam into it until it was dark-brownish red, and handed it to Father. Father silently and grandly accepted the glass, and only then Mother addressed him:

"Tell me, Benche, explain to me what goes on in your head. Do you really think that the king and the senate in Petersburg, where they declare wars, reckon with the felt boots that you will make? Without them you think they won't send soldiers to Port Arthur?"

Father sipped his tea silently.

"Here is a shoemaker," Mother went on unperturbed, "stuck away amid forests and fields, here in the Pinsk swamps, and he refuses to sole felt boots. Why? Because there is shooting going on. When wasn't there shooting going on? But you don't want soldiers to wear the boots you made when they shoot. You want a new order in the world. So what do you do? You refuse to sole felt boots. I get the sense of it: the soldiers can't go to war without boots, not in the snows of Manchuria, and you probably think that the whole world will resound with the news: Yerucham Ben-Zion the shoemaker refuses to sole felt boots and stops the war."

Mother's sarcasm stung Father into a retort: "I don't want the world to talk about me."

"Don't you fear, my husband," Mother ironically reassured him. "The world won't know you and nobody will praise you. Who will know of your madness? Only your wife and children will suffer."

Father said nothing.

"You know I like everything to make sense. So I want to ask you two questions. First, how can you be so cruel to your children? And second, what is the sense of not soling

228

felt boots? Do you think the work will not get done without you? Isn't the war going on without your boots?"

"You must understand, Mehre," Father said. "Supposing all the shoemakers in the world refused to do the work, what could they do in Petersburg? Could they send barefoot soldiers to the Amur? The soldiers would refuse to go; and if they obeyed, the fools would freeze right away."

"But all the shoemakers do sole felt boots," Mother said resentfully.

And as if the thought had been troubling him for months, Father exploded: "But someone must be first to refuse!"

Mehre lowered her head. She felt spent, realizing that she would not dissuade Father, that he was possessed with the idea and would not relinquish it. In a defeated tone she added: "And it is my luck that you should be that first one!"

She began to cry quietly, choking her sobs within herself, as one cries for something lost irretrievably. Father looked at her, seemed on the verge of saying something, but changed his mind. He opened the *siddur* and began to sing the after-Sabbath hymn: "At the end of the day of rest, provide deliverance to Thy people. . . ."

To this day Shimon recalls vividly the image of Father over his *siddur,* and Mother opposite him crying softly. Father seemed so alone that evening, like Abraham who was the only Jew in the world; but Abraham had the promise of God to uphold him in his aloneness, while Father lacked even this.

28. *The Miracle*

On one side the town faced on the Polesyeh swamps, which began right after the last house and stretched for many miles, covered with brush and long, flat weeds. In the springtime, the weeds were good to eat. When one of them was opened, there was a long, whitish, ribbon-like matter inside that was sweet and tasted like fresh bread. Children wandered through the swamps to gather this delicacy. They knew every firm foothold in the swamps. But after such trips they frequently suffered from a rash of reddish spots on their legs. Seldom did a child pass the summer without suffering from this rash.

The swamps were traversed by deep ditches in which fresh water flowed, and in these ditches there was an abundance of all kinds of fish as well as frogs, crayfish, snakes, turtles, and giant water bugs. The swamps also abounded in waterfowl and a variety of other animals. The bushes that grew in the swamp bore bright red poisonous berries. In summer a dense fog hung over the swamp and the air was full of the sounds of all the animals. At sundown and at dawn the fog would be especially thick. At night lights wandered among the bushes, alternately growing bigger and smaller, then vanishing only to reappear again. Everyone believed that these were souls from purgatory wandering about in search of salvation.

Strangers who came to town in the spring or in the fall

would suffer from fever, but the local inhabitants were immune to the ailment.

On the opposite side the town bordered on the Polesyeh forests which extended far, far away. Groves of pine alternated with stands of walnut and birch. Now and then there was a stand of ancient oaks. The forest was dotted with beautiful, deep lakes surrounded by willows that dipped their branches in the water.

The swamp and the forest were a source of terror to the people. When it rained, and especially if the rain was accompanied by wind, the forest roared and many noises came from the dense fog. On such dark nights devils and demons invaded the town and looked for victims. There was not a man, woman or child in town who had not at one time or another seen a devil, or a demon, or a ghost, or some ordinary little long-tailed member of the unclean tribe.

On dark or rainy nights people feared to go outside. But fortunately they believed that there existed a tested protection against the devils—*tzitzis* (the fringes on the small prayer-shawl worn by all Orthodox male Jews all the time). Women and girls who had need to go outside in the evening were therefore accompanied by a man or a boy who, by his very presence—or rather by the presence of the *tzitzis* which he wore—served as protector.

The town clung to all sorts of superstitions, and had its remedies for all the possible evils. Thus there were specialists at reciting incantations against the evil eye, and there were those who had the power to "fix" a strayed cow which failed to return home from pasture with the herd. In such a case the practitioner mumbled an incantation and then drove a knife into the wall. This act "fixed" the missing animal wherever it was so that it should not wander any farther and also be immune to attacks from wolves or bears. When the animal was finally found, it was proof that the charm had worked—the finders saw a small area

231

on its hide, the size of the knife used by the enchanter, bare of hair.

There were all kinds of remedies against disease. To protect children from scarlet fever, measles, small pox, or the evil eye, a red ribbon was put around their necks. Water was never drunk from a jug without first spilling some on the ground—an offering to the evil spirits that dwelt in the water. Bread that had been gnawed by mice was believed to be a good remedy for toothache. Buttons were never sewn on a garment that was being worn at the time, for fear of getting the person's reasoning powers mixed up in the thread. This dire possibility could be obviated by using a thread that was not knotted at the end, or, in the case of a child, by giving it something to chew while the button was being sewn on.

The town had an abundance of birds which nested everywhere: on the roofs, under the eaves, in the trees and in the gardens. The birds were carefully watched by young and old because their behavior often foretold future events. Thus, when ravens crowed it was a bad omen, but when pigeons cooed it was a good omen. The hammering of a woodpecker was an indication of good news on the way. Swallows were most detested, because according to tradition they set fire to the Temple. (Their yellow beaks were believed to contain sulphur.) Pigeons, on the other hand, tried to put out the fire of the burning Temple by bringing water in their beaks. When swallows flew up high and then dived down, children knew that a rainstorm was coming and that some house or barn would be set afire by lightning.

Jews believed all these superstitions just like their Gentile neighbors, but with this difference, that they also believed that all the evil spirits that inhabited the countryside, not excluding Asmodeus, the king of the devils, and Lilith, their queen, were emissaries of God and subject to His will. The Jewish community therefore had no witches or wizards in its midst, though there was no dearth of all kinds of experts at incantation. Witchcraft meant opposing

232

the will of God. Besides, they believed that reciting a Psalm or a page of the *Gemora* could undo any witchcraft.

God was not a remote being to the Jews of the town. He was a kind Father who looked after everyone. And the Torah was not merely something to read, or even to study in order to acquire wisdom; it was a guide and protector. God, Torah, and the Jews—these were the three main pillars of existence.

In order to learn what the future held in store, there was no better guide then a verse from the sacred writings. The statement in the Talmud that: "If upon awakening, a verse occurs to one, this is a minor form of prophecy," was believed implicitly. Boys as well as older men therefore tried to penetrate the curtain of future events by means of verses. The boys had their own technique. To know the end of a matter they would open any sacred volume at random. If the first word on the page (or the first word of the first new verse on that page, depending on the "condition" mentally made in advance) began with a *mem,* it was a good sign, because the word *mazal* (luck) begins with a *mem.* If the first word began with a *nun* the matter was in doubt, because a *nun* could mean either *nes* (miracle) or *nein* (no). If the first word began with a *reish* it was a bad sign, because it signified *ra'* (evil). Sometimes the first attempt was supposed to be conclusive; at other times only three attempts decided the matter. There was considerable cheating. A boy might mentally decide that the first attempt should be conclusive, yet when he opened the book and the first letter proved to be a *reish,* he would announce that he had really intended the third time to be conclusive.

That fall Shimon's older brother, Simcha, had to report for the draft. The entire week that Simcha and Father were in Yurievich, where the draft commission met, Shimon spent trying to discover whether Simcha would be taken into the army or not. He had heard it said at home and outside that if Simcha appeared before the board he would most certainly be drafted. The only hope lay in his not being called at all. Simcha had a second-class deferment, and if the quota of Jewish recruits was to be filled from the other draftees, those with deferments would not come up for an examination.

Simcha was a tall, broad-shouldered, handsome young man. His hands were powerful, and his dense, curly hair was admired by all. He could give a blow and take one with equal ease. He could pick up a two-hundred-pound sack of flour as if it were a pillow.

When the time approached for Simcha to report for the draft, there was much talk at home about the desirability of his maiming himself, or starving himself to lose weight and strength. It was Mother who unequivocally turned down all these suggestions. If it was fated that Simcha should not serve in the army, she maintained, he would escape this ordeal without inflicting injury on himself. And she cited an example to prove her point. Simcha's father had had a first-degree deferment, and in addition had purposely injured his foot. But it was his fate to be a soldier, and when his time came, there were not enough new recruits and even those with a first-degree deferment were called up, and he was drafted. He then served the full five-year term, and all that was left of his efforts to escape army service was a bad leg for the rest of his life. It was necessary to rely on God's mercy, she used to conclude.

Mother had her way, and Simcha's fate was left in the hands of God. Thus Shimon sat in heder, but his mind was in Yurievich where the recruits were being selected. What was going on there? Shimon looked for omens, for some sign from God. He closed his eyes and opened a Bible. When he opened his eyes, he was cheered. The first letter on the page was a *mem*. He knew that it would be folly to tempt fate, but he needed some confirmation, some assurance that the first test was not an accident. He tried

234

again and again, five times altogether, and each time the page began with a *mem*. More than that, the words themselves were significant. The first time the word was *masah* —prophecy; then came *melech*—king; the third time it was *me'eretz Kittim*—from the land of Kittim; the fourth time it was *mah d'var Adonai*—what is the word of God; the last time it was *misgav ladah*—a fortress for the poor. It was evident that a miracle was about to happen. Indeed, the good news came on the very next day: Simcha had drawn the number before the last in the lottery, which put him virtually in the class of first-degree deferment.

Day followed day and no further news came. Again Shimon looked for omens, but now these appeared in confusing order. First there was a *nun*, which indicated a doubtful outcome, and twice thereafter the first letter was a *reish*, definitely a bad sign. There was still hope, for after the two evil omens came a *mem*.

Four more days passed. Shimon was in heder studying Scriptures with his group. They were reading the last chapter of Amos; Shimon intoned the verse and the Rebbe explained it: "Behold I will command and I will shake the House of Israel that is among the nations as one shakes a sieve and not a pebble shall fall to the ground. This means that just as a sieve is shaken to get rid of the dust and sand, but the grains of corn and the pebbles remain, thus when the redemption comes only the saints will remain alive and happy, but the wicked will be cast out like the refuse that is sifted out."

Shimon objected: "But a sieve does the exact opposite! When flour is sifted, the fine flour passes through the openings whereas the refuse remains in the sieve. I see this every day at home."

The Rebbe had a ready answer: "The Scriptures do not refer to a sieve in which flour is sifted, but one in which grains of corn are sifted. When such a sieve is shaken, only that which is of value remains in it, while the chaff which is worthless, like the wicked, is allowed to pass through the openings."

Shimon was not satisfied: "But the verse says 'A pebble,' and this would indicate that also those who are worthless will be saved."

"This was already pointed out by *Targum Yonathan*," the Rebbe said. "But this might be taken to mean that anyone of weight—even if he is not a perfect saint—would also be saved. Perhaps this is how we should understand this verse; for God is merciful and never enforces the severity of the law."

Even as the Rebbe gave his labored explanation it occurred to Shimon that the verse had some significance for the fate of his brother. Simcha would be saved from service in the army. He visualized an enormous sieve being shaken, but instead of grains of corn the sieve contained young men called up for the draft. He saw them falling through the openings in the sieve directly into the hands of the officials; but Simcha remains in the sieve, his arms outspread and laughing.

Suddenly there was a tumult in the street and people started running from all sides in the direction of Shimon's home. Now he knew for sure that his brother had been freed. The boys in heder became restless and even before Shimon came out of his trance, Rochel-Leah ran in all out of breath, "Come, Shimon, come home," she shouted. "Simcha is back with a white ticket."

Shimon rose and calmly walked out with his sister. She looked at him in amazement. "You're a cool one," she said.

"I knew it all the time," he answered matter-of-factly.

"How did you know?" she asked in disbelief.

"There were signs," he said cryptically.

"In that case you are a wicked one, a real Haman, you have the heart of a Tartar. You knew it all the time, so why didn't you tell Mother?"

Shimon tried to excuse himself:

"At first I wasn't sure myself. Five times in a row the

236

signs were good, then there was doubt, then again a good sign. Now I see it all clearly. The good signs at first meant that Simcha would draw a high number in the lottery. Then the doubt when his number was called up, and in the end the good sign showing that he would be freed. I only understood it when the Rebbe explained the significance of the pebbles that would not go through the sieve."

"I can't understand what you're jabbering, but if you knew and didn't tell Mother you are wicked."

"I told you," Shimon explained, "that I didn't know for sure till just a few minutes ago, just before you came in . . ." He stopped abruptly realizing how foolish his words sounded.

But Rochel-Leah would not be placated. "You knew something and you didn't tell. And maybe you're just boasting. Anyway, come home quickly. There's a big to-do there. Father and Simcha returned from Yurievich by post express."

The house was packed. A bottle of liquor and some cakes were on the table. Shimon saw Gneshe-Reitse puttering around in the kitchen and understood where the cake came from in the middle of the week. Gneshe-Reitse always had cake on hand. This was her livelihood, to provide cakes for unexpected weekday festivities, though she did it more for the sake of the merit of the good deed then for the few pennies she made. Simcha was seated at the head of the table and recounted what had happened in Yurievich. This was obviously not the first time he told his story for he repeated it very fluently.

"So I had a second-class deferment," he said, "and I drew a high number, and I had nothing to worry about. I stayed at the hostel perfectly calm. Last year even some without deferments were not called up. Of course, there were rumors in town that this year things were different—not enough recruits, because Jews were running to America.

237

On the other hand, there was good news for me when I heard that the draft board accepted recruits right and left —as long as one had the strength to walk in on his own feet they stamped his papers 'Fit.' So I was glad. And then it became clear that this year the second-degree deferments would be called. But I still didn't lose hope—they would not get to me, because considering the number I drew I was practically a first-degree deferment. So I didn't even look into the draft office.

"But on the fourth day, in the morning, I heard that things looked bad. There was no question now that second deferments would be called up. I still felt sure they wouldn't call me, just the same I thought perhaps I'd better look in there. And just as I was debating with myself whether to go or not, a young man came running with the news that the draft board had been calling second deferments for some time. 'Better hurry there before they call your name,' he said to me.

"So I left the hostel and, outside, one of the draftees tells me that my name had already been called. I started running to the draft office as fast as I could and my heart pounded. Now that my name was called I had no doubt that I would be drafted, but it would be a nice business not only to be drafted, but also to miss the last roll call and Father should have to pay a three hundred ruble fine. We have our own house and a cow and they were sure to collect the fine.

"So I ran breathlessly, and suddenly I see someone running on my right. I looked at the man and he seemed to be in his thirties, a tall and fine looking Jew with a reddish beard and brown eyes. He looked familiar somehow, yet I knew I had never seen him before. Just the same there was something familiar about him. So we ran alongside each other. I thought I'd ask him whether he too was up for the draft, at his age, but then decided it was none of my business. I had plenty of troubles of my own. But it was

238

somehow strange how he ran in step with me. Suddenly he said:

" 'Simcha, don't be so frightened. You will get a white ticket.'

"I looked at him and said angrily: 'And how do you know? Are you a prophet? Who are you? And where do you run?'

"And he answered with a smile that made me feel good all over: 'You can believe everything I tell you. I am not a prophet, but I know what I am talking about. Don't you recognize me?'

" 'I never saw you before,' I said and my breath was pretty short from running and from fright.

"But he answered me mildly: 'It's a wonder that you don't recognize me. Didn't you ever take a good look at yourself in the mirror? We are the exact images of each other. I am your grandfather, Gute-Simcha. Your sister Gitte, and you, both of you are named after me. I died young. I drowned in the Pripet when I carted flour for Passover. Well, when a man dies in such a fashion, while doing a good deed, his word counts in the right places. When your mother came to my grave and told me that you are being called up for the draft, I went to Him Who decides everything in the world and I told Him: I don't want that my grandson, who is named after me, should be a soldier and in war time too. It's enough, I said, that I overlooked my son and let him go in the army. But I will not permit that my grandson should serve *Fonia*. I won't permit it! And I had my way.'

"I stopped," Simcha continued, "because I was completely out of breath, whether from running or from fright. I simply had to stop a moment. I was already close to the draft offices and I heard my name called for the second time, but I simply had to stop and ask something of grandfather."

Here one of the guests, a young man both enlightened

and versed in the works of Maimonides, asked Simcha: "Didn't it occur to you that it was all imagination?"

"I didn't stop to consider the matter," Simcha said. "I saw him with my own eyes. But as soon as I stopped he vanished. Was I surprised? I don't remember. All I recall is that suddenly my limbs became heavy as lead. Each hand weighed half a ton, each foot a full ton. I couldn't run any more. I could barely drag my feet. And I didn't care any more whether I got there on time or not. I didn't care about anything.

"I entered the office just as my name was called for the third and last time. I began to undress and suddenly felt a great pressure on my chest and on my back, and a sharp stab of pain pierced me from the left shoulder down to my fingertips, so that everything turned black before my eyes."

"When I regained consciousness I was lying on a soft table and the doctors were examining me. The pressure lifted from my chest, my head cleared and I sat up. The older doctor told me to get off the table and I jumped off. All the pain was gone too."

" 'Do you often have such pains in the shoulder or in the chest?' he asked me.

"I looked at him. 'What pains?' I said. 'I was never sick and I never had any pains. I don't know what happened now, but it must be nothing. I was just afraid of being late.'

"The doctor smiled. 'You're OK,' he said, and again he pounded my chest and back and listened with his tube and then with his ear. Then he told me to hop twenty times and stopped me after the fifth time and listened again. Then he called another doctor and told him to listen to my heart, and that one only waved his hand and said 'Unfit.' And so I got a white ticket."

A strange figure stands behind Shimon's back as he writes this story of town life. He bends over Shimon's shoulder, reads the lines, and laughs. "You have no cause to be proud

240

of your town Jews," he says. "Just a lot of backwardness and superstition and fear of the unknown. It probably never occurred to them to take Simcha to a doctor, or to suspect that the doctors in the draft office were right and Simcha had suffered a heart attack. Simcha must have died young."

Shimon looks at the stranger, who is a reflection of himself, and says: "Not so fast please. There is more to the picture of the town than this framework. And as for Simcha, do not worry about him. He was taken to a doctor. And at the time this is being written, decades later, I can say with perfect assurance that Simcha can no longer die young. Listen to the end of the story . . ."

The house was crowded with strangers from all over town who had come to share in the festivities. But the two women who had long since appointed themselves in charge of providing for the poor, soon took over. They packed in baskets whatever bread, rolls and beigel they could find, and they began urging the guests to leave. "Enough! Enough!" they shouted. "On Saturday liquor and cake will be served and you will be invited. Now everybody go home and give people a chance to catch their breath."

When the house emptied of strangers, Sime-Dvoire said to Mother:

"And now, Mehre, listen. First of all give us all of Simcha's clothes; his Sabbath outfit, the blue suit, and his short winter coat, and his scarves and his underwear. Just imagine that he was taken into the army and you no longer have any use for his clothes. And also whatever money you have. Imagine that you have to pay a bribe to keep him out of the army in time of war. How much money have you in the house? Seven rubles? You need it to pay for the flour? Hand it over. It's a cheap price for a white ticket."

Mother made no protest and gave whatever was asked of her. Then the smell of fresh bread filled the house. Sime-

Dvoire opened the oven. She saw the bread ready to be taken out and ordered Mother: "Hurry, Mehre, give me the rake. You think I have all day to stay here? I still have to take all these things to the poor."

Quickly she removed the bread from the oven and packed it in the baskets. As she was about to take the last five loaves, Mother intervened: "Sime-Dvoire, I have ten mouths to feed. Don't leave me without a mouthful of bread in the house."

"You'll manage," Sime-Dvoire retorted briefly.

Mother did not know what to do. She plucked at the corners of her kerchief and did not know whether to be angry or not. Finally she said: "Then sell me five loaves of bread."

"You will have to pay twelve kopeks a loaf, the same price you charge in the market-place," Sime-Dvoire said. "It's good bread."

Mother was flattered by the compliment. "You don't have to praise my bread. But you will have to give me the loaves on credit. I haven't a cent left. You took everything."

"Your credit is good," Sime-Dvoire reassured her. "Your credit was always good. Take five loaves of bread, but don't pick the bigger ones. Take them as they come."

Mehre took five loaves from the nearest basket and Sime-Dvoire said to Dreizhe who worked with her: "Mehre owes us five times twelve, a total of sixty kopeks. I forget easily, so you keep it in mind."

Mother was offended: "I won't keep it from you, Sime-Dvoire, don't you worry."

"I know, I know," Sime-Dvoire said. "But it's best to remember and to remind."

The two women took the loaded baskets and went their way to distribute the contents among the poor. Mother sighed happily: "It's been a long time since we ate borrowed bread, but thank God it will be eaten in happiness."

Leiser-Itche, the "enlightened," had prophesied that "when the Czar catches it in Manchuria, the real dance will start here; just you wait and see." He guessed right, but not altogether. Following on the Russo-Japanese war there began the prologue to the drama which did not reach its climax till twelve years later, in 1917.

When the war ended Russia rocked uneasily. Numerous strikes broke out and there were bloody demonstrations in the large cities. In the provinces the peasants revolted and burned the houses of the landowners. The government responded with punitive expeditions against the peasants and with pogroms against Jews. A popular ditty of that time proclaimed:

> "The people asked for bread;
> The Czar replied: Drop dead!"

The great events re-echoed in our town as well. The trains did not come on time, or stopped running altogether for days on end. Prices soared and many products were completely unavailable.

Shimon recalls that wheat flour was then worth its weight in gold, and even corn flour was frequently in short supply. The bakers in town suffered. When on occasion a couple of carloads of flour did arrive, it had to be bought with cash, and even then nobody got as much as he needed or wanted.

Mehre was an exception to this rule. She always obtained as much flour as she wanted, and continued to pay for it once a week on Saturday nights. For years Mehre had been a loyal customer of Reb Rephoel Mosirer, the flour merchant, and now he recompensed her for her loyalty.

Shimon remembers how, during this time, he once went to Reb Rephoel's store-room on an errand for his mother to ask for two more sacks of flour. He entered the store-room and stopped short in the doorway. The dim and dusty expanse of the warehouse was almost entirely empty, and Shimon at once thought of the biblical expression "lay the earth waste." He had never before understood the full significance of the word "waste." He used to imagine a waste place of destruction; but now he realized that it meant simply emptiness, not the emptiness of a house that is about to be inhabited, nor that of a house that had been lived in and is now abandoned, but a meaningless emptiness that breathes of hopelessness. The walls of the warehouse were still covered with flour dust, as were also the small windows high on the walls. On the floor was a grayish mess of flour-dust and mud. A few sacks of flour lay disconsolately in one corner, emphasizing by their insignificance the emptiness about them.

"What are you staring at," Reb Rephoel interrupted Shimon's revery. "It's all right, the place will be full again. Your mother wants two more sacks of flour? Why, I sent her two sackfuls only last Friday."

"There's less than half a sackful left," Shimon told him.

"What does she do with all that flour!" Reb Rephoel wondered within himself. He turned to the boy, "Tell her I will send her one sackful as soon as the porter comes, and I will come to your house in the evening."

Meantime Keile-Reike, who also had a bakery, came in asking for at least a hundred-weight of flour. Rephoel offered her forty pounds. She was displeased and pleaded her case: "Justice!" she cried. "To Mehre you sold four hundred pounds of flour only last Friday, and now I see her scholar is here to ask for more, and you are giving it. Yet she buys on credit."

"Mehre was my customer when prices were low," Rephoel explained calmly. "She never ran around looking for bargains, and she always paid on time, every Saturday night. Her word is her bond, always. So now I am repaying her for her honesty and loyalty all these years."

"Honesty, Loyalty," Keile-Reike sneered. "She makes oodles of money with the flour you now give her. She resells it. Some people have luck, they deceive the world and are considered honest."

"I don't believe it," Rephoel said.

"Find out for yourself," Keile-Reike taunted.

"I will; I will," he assured her.

That evening, after prayers, Reb Rephoel came to Shimon's house. Mehre welcomed him and hurried to get him a glass of tea. But Rephoel refused even to be seated and said irritably: "I didn't come for tea, Mehre. I came to have an argument with you. Today is Tuesday. On Friday afternoon I sent you four hundred pounds of flour. Today I sent another two hundred pounds. You couldn't have used the flour I sent you Friday on that day because it was already late in the day, yet I see that the new sack is already started. Tell me, how can you use up so much flour, almost six hundred pounds in three days."

"Your reckoning is faulty, Reb Rephoel," Mehre said. "I already started tomorrow's dough, so it is four days."

"You can't fool me, Mehre," Rephoel was now angry in earnest. "I heard that you do business behind my back with the flour you buy from me. It's not nice, Mehre; I didn't think you'd do a thing like that."

Shimon watched his mother. She was tense and, as usual in such circumstances, tugged at the corners of her kerchief.

"I see, Mehre," Rephoel sighed, "that the rumor is true.

You say nothing. It's really a shame, and from now on I will give you flour as to all the others, on a dole."

Mother regained some of her composure and now spoke rapidly. "Well, Reb Rephoel, I won't deceive you. I do sell your flour, but I don't earn money on it. I have not become a business woman behind your back. I don't make a cent on your flour."

Rephoel looked at her suspiciously. "You sell it, yet you aren't a business woman; you sell it, yet you don't make a cent on it. When one sells something, one is in business and one makes money on the deal. Nobody buys and sells without profit."

"Please try and understand," Mother said calmly and with certainty in her voice. "I do sell the flour, and I do profit on it, and still I am not in business. My profit consists in gaining a good deed, and this *mitzvah* I will gladly share with you. God is my witness."

"Well, this is a mystery, so, bring on the glass of tea, I am curious to hear what this is all about, how you sell flour and gain only a *mitzvah*."

Mehre served the tea and asked Rephoel: "Do you know Beile the widow?" Rephoel waved his hand deprecatingly: "I know her like a bad penny."

"Yes, I know," Mehre said resentfully. "You all love her like smoke in the eyes. Who does love an embittered pauper? She was never a good credit risk. How could she have been when she never had a cent to her name. She has five daughters to support, so she was always in debt; and if she ever had a penny, she had to look for bargains. Now all the merchants are remembering her past sins. Wherever she goes to buy flour, there are others who take precedence over her. If I didn't share my flour with her she would starve to death. Here is a widow with five grown daughters, and in an entire Jewish community no one is concerned about it."

"Does she pay you for the flour at least?" Rephoel asked.

"Me she pays on time," Mehre said.

Reb Rephoel sighed: "See that your *mitzvah* doesn't cost you too much, and don't forget that you have ten mouths to feed yourself. And, above all, be careful that my other customers don't find out about it or there will be no end of complaints."

"I'll keep it secret," Mehre promised. "Just the same I think it is a great wrong that no flour is sold to her. A widow with five daughters must not be left without help. Such a big Jewish community, and three synagogues full of worshipers, but when it comes to the main thing, risking a few pennies, it is worse than Sodom, may God forgive me for my words."

Rephoel laughed. "You and your husband are a pair. Both of you look for justice in the world. You want to remake the world."

But Mehre did not like the comparison. "Nothing of the sort," she said. "He did not want to sole felt boots, but that didn't stop the shooting on the Amur. But in this case, if it weren't for me, a widow would starve to death and no one else would lift a finger to put a feather to her nose to see whether she is ready to be buried."

Reb Rephoel rose to go. "All the same," he said good-naturedly, "I repeat that God sits above and makes matches below. You are no wiser than your husband. Just look at the two of you, two paupers, a shoemaker and a baker woman, and you don't like the way the world is ordered. But believe me, I do delight in the two of you."

He went up to the door and was about to kiss the *mezuzah* and walk out, when he turned around and remarked: "Remember, Mehre, what I told you. Not a word to anyone that you share your flour with Beile or I will never hear the last of it from my other customers. Good night."

The above would be a nice story, Shimon now thinks to himself, even if this were all there was to it. But there is an epilogue to it, and it is good that it is so, otherwise the reader might get the impression that Shimon's parents were the sole saints in town; that they were "the apple trees among the trees of the forest." This was not so. Righteousness was the norm in the town. Everyone envied and admired the honest, the good and the pious. Naturally, not everyone achieved a state of honesty, piety and goodness, any more than everyone is rich in a society in which wealth is admired.

On the eve of Shevuos the widow burst into Mehre's house shouting: "Mehre, you must save me!"

"What is the matter?" Mehre was alarmed.

"A misfortune, a great calamity, a thunder from heaven has struck me," Beile intoned in a loud voice. "You know that I take two loads of bread every day to the Gentiles working at the station. So my Soreh took the two baskets— they were so heavy she had to hire a cart and pay fifteen kopeks. So far so good. But the foreman at the station tells her they must have another forty pounds of bread tomorrow. So my Soreh says to him tomorrow is Shevuos, a holiday; so he says, in that case bring them later today. Why all of a sudden? Another gang of workers has to arrive on a late train. So my Soreh says to him, 'Where will we get more bread? There is no flour in town, and besides, even if we got some, there isn't time to sour the dough and bake it before sundown and tomorrow is a holiday.' So the foreman tells her, 'Don't bother me with your Jewish holiday; I can get bread somewhere else.' And you know what this means—he will get bread from the Gentile baker. That's all I need—I'd never again sell any bread at the station."

"It's a bad situation," Mehre answered, "but how can I help you? You know that I shared my flour with you. See for yourself, there, the kitchen is clean of flour just like on the eve of Pesach. And my white bread is mostly sold already. I doubt there will be a few pounds left. A sudden demand for bread today! What can I do? Help you sigh?"

"No, Mehre," the widow said gently. "I know what I am talking about. Do you think I am blind? I don't want flour from you. What good would flour do me now? Just promise me that you won't get angry and I will tell you how you can help me."

Mehre looked at the woman with surprise. "Why should I get angry? You know very well that I will help you if only I can."

"I am not so sure," the widow said in a singsong. "We'll see if you get angry or not."

"Come to the point," Mehre said with some impatience. "What are you driving at?"

The widow pointed with her finger. "Here is a dough all kneaded. There is more than forty pounds of it. I could bake it in an hour or two and deliver it."

Mother answered wrathfully: "Did you lose your mind? She says calmly, 'here is a dough all kneaded.' This is the dough for my Shevuos rolls! As though you didn't know it!"

"See! You did get angry" the widow exclaimed triumphantly. "Just look at how angry you are!"

"Who's angry!" Mehre cried. "Just the same, tell me what gave you such an idea. What kind of a holiday will I have without dairy rolls?"

The widow burst into tears. "And what kind of a holiday will I have if the Gentile baker takes away my livelihood? And what do you think will I and my daughters eat this Shevuos? Plain black bread! But you must have rolls! You must have everything. Not enough that you have a husband, a son a scholar, and a cow that calved! But what have I? Five grown daughters, the youngest of which should have heard her wedding music five years ago."

Mehre paled at the sight of the sobbing widow, and bit her lips. At last she despairingly shook her head and said: "Take the dough and stop bewailing me. I'll manage somehow, or I'll do this Shevuos without rolls. Anyway they would now stick in our throats."

The widow's tears dried at once and she called to her two oldest daughters who stood waiting for her outside. "Come and help carry the dough."

As soon as the three left, Mehre said to Shimon: "What will we do now? Run to the market-place and see if Rochel-Leah has any rolls left. If she has, tell her to bring them home at once."

But no rolls were left. They had been sold to the last one. Mother ran to Reb Rephoel and told him of her plight. He listened attentively, then burst out laughing. "I can only repeat what I said before," he said. "You flew into a rage when your husband refused to sole felt boots for the army. But you are no better than he is. To look at you, one might think you are a smart woman, but deep within you there is a simpleton."

Mother was insulted: "You have no right to preach to me, Reb Rephoel. What should I do if I can't withstand the tears of a widow? And as for my husband's refusing to sole felt boots for the army, who stood and wept over him? Stop preaching. Better tell me whether you have any flour for me."

The merchant chuckled: "It would only be right to teach you a lesson and let you hunger together with your children for a couple of days. But I will let it pass this time. I have a couple of sacks of flour. The rolls won't look very appetizing, but they won't taste so bad. Take as much of the flour as you want."

On the second day of Shevuos, late in the afternoon, Beile the widow came to Mehre's house. Her face shone with happiness. She stopped in the middle of the sitting room, folded her hands in front of her apron and said: "Well, Mehre, and how much will you charge me for the dough?"

"Why this settling of accounts during the holiday?" Mehre was surprised.

"I can't wait till the day is over," Beile said. "I'm anxious to know how much you will charge me, down to the last cent. But I want to tell you something interesting, something you'd never have expected."

Mehre was chagrined. "It can wait till after the holiday. Anyway, what's there to reckon? You know how much flour I used for the dough, and you know the price of flour these days."

But Beile would not accept such a simple answer. "No," she said. "This time you guessed wrong. This time you will charge me also for the yeast and the salt and the whey and the piece of butter you put into the dough—for everything. And you will get a ruble and a half on top of it all."

Mother looked at her in disbelief. "How come you are throwing money around like this all of a sudden? Where did you get the extra ruble and a half?"

"I want to show you," Beile said proudly, "that Beile Aaron-Nohum's isn't what people say she is. I know, I know they say I don't pay my debts, and I am a tough customer—always looking for a bargain, and I make life miserable for everyone. What don't they say about me! So I want to show you that when God helps me I am no worse than others. Don't interrupt me and I will tell you a nice story. The rolls I baked from your dough made a hit with the laborers. 'These aren't rolls,' they said, 'but cakes.' They were properly drunk and they gave my Soreh a tip of three rubles. 'We are honest men,' they said, 'and we don't pay the price of rolls for cake. We won't deceive a poor woman.' My Soreh refused to take the tip, but they forced it on her. 'What do you mean you won't take it? Are you trying to shame us?' they said."

"A three-ruble tip?" Mother could not believe her ears.

"Yes, three rubles, may I not live to see my daughters married if I don't tell the truth. So that's what I say: This time we go fifty-fifty with you. If it weren't for your dough, where would I be? I want to show everybody that I am not as bad as they think I am. It's just that I am always in such

251

trouble; but that, if God helps, I, too, know what fairness is."

"Thank you very much, Beile," Mother said calmly. "It's very nice of you. But I won't sell my *mitzvah* for a ruble and a half. The tip is all yours."

"Don't play the saint," Beile sneered. "A ruble and a half is not something to sneeze at."

But Mehre was adamant. "Listen to me, Beile. I gave you the bread out of my children's mouths. This Shevuos I have rocks instead of dairy rolls. I gave you the dough because I couldn't bear to see you cry, and I hoped God would account it a good deed for me. Now you want to pay me on the spot for it. No! I won't sell my *mitzvah*."

At this point Beile raised an outcry. "Just look at the plaster saint! You'll earn a bigger *mitzvah* if you buy a pair of shoes for your scholar. He goes about with his toes sticking out."

"Not with this kind of money," Mehre protested.

Beile flew into a rage. "Not with this kind of money. What is the matter with this money? To hear you talk one might think my daughter got it some sinful way. It is kosher money honestly earned. We knead and we bake and we drag heavy baskets to the station. Every cent is dipped in blood, not in sweat, and she calls it 'this kind of money.' You'll take the money, just you wait and see."

Shimon expected his mother to fly into a rage, but to his surprise she did not lose her composure. "You can shout all you want," she said to Beile. "But I will not take your money. I don't sell my *mitzvos*."

Beile burst into tears. "I have sworn we would share it half-and-half. Can't I too have a *mitzvah*? Must you have everything? A husband, a son a scholar, and your cow calved and giving a lot of milk, may no evil eye befall her; and in addition you must also have a lot of *mitzvos* for the hereafter. But what have I got? Five daughters and a lot of heartache. It won't hurt you to let me have a little *mitzvah* too. You want everything."

"What do you want from me?" Mother was becoming irritated. "This time your tears won't help you. I'm telling you for the last time. I don't sell my *mitzvos*."

"But I have made a vow!" Beile protested.

"Then go to the rabbi and let him absolve you of your vow."

A crowd began to gather outside before the open windows. Beile started screaming still louder, "You are mean! You have the heart of a Tartar! A person could die right before you and you wouldn't give him a drink of water! You want everything for yourself!"

"Don't shout, please," Mehre begged. "What harm have I ever done to you in all my life! People will come running from all over town, the way you scream. They will think I robbed you or something. Shame on you!"

But Beile would not give in. "Let them come. Let the whole world know your wickedness. I have nothing to be ashamed of. You be ashamed! I'll stick my head out of the window and tell everything to the whole world."

She turned to the window as if to implement her threat, and she noticed Reb Getzel coming down the street. "I know what I will do," she said. "I'll call him in and let him judge between us."

Mehre tried to stop her, but was too late.

Reb Getzel came in. Mother stood shamed. "Sit down, Reb Getzel," she muttered. "And as long as you came into my house, let me serve tea. It wasn't my idea to bother you. It was against my will that you were called. But now that you are here, please tell her to let me alone. She will listen to you."

Beile raised her hand: "Don't you decide for Reb Getzel what should be done," she warned Mehre. "Serve the tea and let him hear both of us."

Reb Getzel sat down, looked at the two women with his wise eyes, opened his snuff box, inhaled a pinch and sneezed. Then he said, "I have heard that the two of you are great friends and suddenly there is a quarrel, on a

253

holiday too, so that you must have someone to judge between you. What's the matter? You can't share out your treasures in peace?"

Mehre sighed: "Rebbe, she has latched onto me and I can't get rid of her. She insists that . . ."

Beile interrupted her: "Mehre, you have such a welcome guest, why don't you serve your tasty rolls? And where is your *Babke*?"

Mother flushed and Reb Getzel scolded Beile: "Shame on you! Are you trying to insult her? And if there are no fine rolls, does it mean that Shevuos is no longer a holiday?"

But Beile was firm in her righteousness: "I am not shaming her, Rebbe. But just look at her, red as a beet! And do you know why? You think she has rolls? Rocks she has, not rolls. And do you know why? Because she gave me the dough she had prepared for the holiday."

And Beile recounted the entire story without missing a detail. She talked quickly and loudly. Reb Getzel relaxed in his chair, and the more Beile talked, the more his face glowed. When she had finished, he turned to Mehre: "Is it true?"

"It is true," Mehre admitted. "Beile is a loud-mouth, but not a liar."

Reb Getzel smiled broadly and stroked his beard. "In that case, women," he said, "listen to me. Such a case already happened once long ago. The Midrash relates that when Alexander the Great came to the land of Kochi, there came two men before the king of Kochi with a dispute. One man said, I have bought a field from my neighbor who now stands before you and when I began to plow it I found a treasure buried in it. So I told him about it and asked him to take the treasure because I had bought a field and not a treasure. But he insists that he sold me the field and everything in it.

"Then the king of Kochi asked the first man: 'Do you

have a daughter of marriageable age?' and the man said 'Yes.'

"And the king of Kochi asked the other man: 'Do you have a son of marriageable age?' and the man said 'Yes.'

"Thereupon the king said: 'Let the son of the one marry the daughter of the other and let them have the treasure.'

"What I mean to say," Reb Getzel pursued his talk, "is that your case is not unlike the one I just told you about. True, in the story a treasure was involved, whereas your dispute concerns a ruble and a half. In the story the parties had a son and a daughter, and this does not apply to you. So my judgment will be a little different. Beile will give you the ruble and a half, and you, Mehre, will buy flour with it and bake bread and distribute it to the poor. In this manner Beile will observe her vow and you, Mehre, will not receive compensation for your *mitzvah*. Well, women, are you satisfied with my judgment?"

"Satisfied," both women nodded their heads in approval.

Reb Getzel looked about himself and saw the poverty of the house and he added: "You, Mehre, need not distribute all the bread for the ruble and a half. You may keep a few loaves as the cost of your labor."

Mehre answered without hesitation: "I don't want the bread of charity. Thank God, I don't need charity."

Reb Getzel rose, went to the door, kissed the *mezuzah*, and in parting added, "A happy holiday to both of you. God grant that there should be more disputes like this among Jews. Now, say Amen."

As soon as he left the house, Beile announced triumphantly: "Well? Who had her way?"

But Mehre answered impatiently: "You are intolerable. You always look for quarrels. Enough is enough. And as for my Shimon, he does not go about with his toes sticking out. He has new shoes for the holiday."

"Yes, everybody knows how rich you are," Beile jeered. "I suppose you eat meat on weekdays. So, if he has shoes, he needs a suit. But a judgment is a judgment. Now serve tea, and don't bother bringing out the rolls."

As he wrote the above, Shimon thought: Cynics will say that this is a lot of romanticism. Were I to tell about evil and wickedness and passions, it would be "realism."

Also, now Shimon understands why Reb Getzel did not tell the two women the end of the Midrash. In the Midrash the story ends in this wise: When Alexander the Great heard the judgment of the king of Kochi, he was amazed. "Why are you surprised?" the king of Kochi asked him. "Didn't I judge correctly?" "Yes, very righteously," Alexander said. "And how would you have judged in your kingdom?" "In my kingdom," Alexander said, "I would have ordered the two men beheaded and taken the gold to the royal treasury." Whereupon the king of Kochi asked: "Does the sun shine in your country? And does it rain in your land?" "Yes," Alexander answered. And the king of Kochi asked further: "Are there sheep and cattle in your kingdom?" "Yes," Alexander answered. "Then it must be that the sun shines and the rain falls in your country on account of the innocent sheep and cattle, because the people do not deserve it."

Reb Getzel did not tell the end of the story because Beile and Mehre were not exceptions in town.

30. *New Horizons*

One sunny afternoon Shimon saw Eisik the tailor running from the railway station. He was terribly excited. He dashed across the bridge and ran to the market-place. He leaped to the porch of Beile-Broche's house and began shouting incoherently: "Jews! Good news for Jews! Good news for Jews! A Constitution! The Czar has granted a Constitution! Now we will all be happy! A Constitution! A Constitution!"

His disjointed outcries had an indescribable effect. People came running from all sides. Moshe Gerstein dashed off to the station to check on the news and soon returned with the glad confirmation—a telegram had indeed come from Petrograd announcing the new constitution.

But the happiness which was caused by Eisik's glad tidings did not last long. A short time later the word "Pogrom" began to be whispered in town. Rechitse and Homel, two neighboring towns, had pogroms. The one in Rechitse came suddenly, but the one in Homel had been anticipated and the Jewish community in town had organized a strong self-defense. It proved to be useless. The armed Jewish young men and women who came from neighboring towns were met by a company of infantry. All of them were arrested. Those who resisted were shot.

For the first time in Shimon's memory, the Jews of Kalinkovich were afraid of their peasant neighbors. Normally they were not worried, even on Fair days, when peasants got drunk and there were many fights. The Jewish community in Kalinkovich had many laborers, men who could give as well as they received and who were not afraid of a fight. But now fear seized everyone. Rumors were rife. It was said that more than a hundred armed blackguards were to be brought from the provincial capitol by the authorities, and that a company of regular troops was to be brought to prevent the Jews from defending themselves. It was rumored that agitators had been visiting the villages and inciting the peasants with tales that the Jews were planning to set fire to the big church on the day of the annual great Fair some weeks later, and that the peasants were asked to come to town on that day armed with axes and scythes to protect their church. The provincial governor was behind all this agitation, the rumors declared—he wanted to get even with the Jewish community in Kalinkovich for having become a revolutionary nest.

That Saturday the old Bes Midrash was in turmoil. The "Democrats" halted the reading of the Torah and seized the platform. A young man from a nearby town pounded the table and shouted: "We will not let them slaughter us like sheep! We will fight! We have a self-defense organization, but we lack weapons! The congregation must assign five hundred rubles for weapons! There must be no delay! Time is short!"

The young man's brief speech caused a storm. Older men shouted: "Insolence! Not enough that you brought misfortune on us with your secret societies, now you want weapons to shed more blood!"

The two parties nearly came to blows; but at this point Moishe Gerstein, who owned a haberdashery store, intervened. "You talk of conspiracy, and now you come before an entire congregation to demand five hundred rubles from the treasury," he said to the young men. "Fools that you are! Do you want us all to rot in Siberia? Next I suppose

258

you will ask that we sign and notarize an agreement to give you the money! You are not revolutionists! You are fools!"

The young men left and there was no more open talk about arms. But later it was quietly whispered that money had been given for arms.

The following Saturday, Moishe-Dovid said to Shimon: "It's time you met Yoseph-Haim Doroshkin. Come to my house at three this afternoon and we will go to see him."

Yoseph-Haim Doroshkin lived in his sister's house in the long street. He was known throughout the district as the outstanding Zionist and Hebraist of the neighborhood. He contributed articles to *Hamelitz* and engaged in polemics with S. Bernfeld. Since childhood his legs were paralyzed. His arms were spindly and distorted and he could not hold a book or write except with great difficulty. Speaking Hebrew was a matter of principle with him, and he never uttered a word of Yiddish to anyone who understood Hebrew. His room was filled with innumerable books, magazines and newspapers which he received from all over the world. The non-revolutionary youth of the town spent most of their time in his house. Later, when Shimon returned from the *yeshivah*, he, too, became a regular visitor.

Yoseph-Haim lived according to Jewish tradition. He had a beard and *peios* and never went about with uncovered head. He always had a *minyan* in his house; nevertheless, he was not considered pious in town. Whenever some young man began attending his *minyan*, he would be taunted: "So now you've stopped praying."

When Shimon arrived together with Moishe-Dovid, he found his friends and all the town *maskilim* in Yoseph-Haim's house. They had carried him in his bed into the living room and they formed a circle about him. A young man whom Shimon did not know held a green pamphlet which he was about to read to them. Yoseph-Haim made some introductory remarks. "Meier will now read you

Chaim-Nachman Bialik's *The Burden of Nemirov*," he said. "Bialik wrote this poem after the pogrom in Kishinev, and it is this pogrom that he describes. But the censor would not allow its publication unless it was named *The Burden of Nemirov,* ostensibly a description of the slaughter that took place in Khmelnitski's time. But everyone can take the hint."

This was the first time that Shimon heard anyone talk grammatical Hebrew and it sounded strange to his ears. He understood every word, but he found it hard to link these words, which in his mind were associated with passages from the Bible, with current events. Little by little he overcame this strangeness and became engrossed in what the young man was reading; and the more he heard of it, the more he disliked the poem. The first expression which struck him like a blow was "a Jew and his dog." Since when did Jews have dogs? he could not help thinking with irritation. Was the author trying to be insulting? The farther it went, the worse it became. The poet was blaming the Jews—it was their fault. They were more to blame than the murderers, because they offered no resistance.

When the reading was over, there was much applause; and this, too, Shimon did not like. What was the occasion for applause after a poem about a pogrom? Then Doroshkin spoke with passion about the need for self-defense. He also discussed the poem with tears in his eyes.

It was getting late in the afternoon and those present constituted themselves a *minyan* and prayed *Minhah.* Now Shimon understood why people in town joked about this *minyan.* Yoseph-Haim was the only one there who truly prayed. The others mostly chatted, and it was curious to see how quickly they finished their *Shmoneh Esre.*

Shimon was depressed and silent as he left the house with Moishe-Dovid. The latter noticed his silence and challenged him: "Why all the silence? It's not in your nature. Anything upset you?"

"Yes, the poem," Shimon answered briefly.

"What?" Moishe-Dovid was surprised.

"The poem," Shimon repeated.

"How is that?"

"The poet reproves the Jews; yet he should have chastised the Goyim."

"But it is a deserved reproof," Moishe-Dovid argued. "How could they run to hide? How could they see their wives and mothers and sisters raped before their eyes and remain in their hiding places? They should have felt like Samson: 'Perish my soul together with the Philistines.'"

"Was the author there?" Shimon asked. "And how does he know that he would have acted otherwise? It is not right to talk this way about Jews," Shimon concluded angrily.

"You mean there should be no resistance?"

"I didn't say that."

"Then why didn't they resist?"

"How could they have expected a pogrom? Did they have weapons? Now that it has happened once, we know we may expect it again."

"Would you say it is all right to hide in pigsties and other filthy places?" Moishe-Dovid said and quoted from Bialik's poem.

"I don't know. Perhaps I would do the same, and maybe the poet would also run to hide and save his life. All I know is that Rabbi Yoseph Hacohen tells in *Emek Habocho* how many Jews did resist their attackers and spat at their idols and were murdered, while others hid under their beds and were stabbed to death, and he calls all of them martyrs. He calls on God to pass judgment. He does not ridicule Jews, nor does he slander them that they tried to cash in on their wounds."

Moishe-Dovid stared at Shimon in disbelief. "Reb Getzel says of you," he began, "that you are a level-headed reasoner. But it seems to me that you are simply contrary. The whole world raves about Bialik's poem, and you, Shimon ben Yerucham, have the audacity to say that you don't like it. Better keep quiet or people will laugh at you."

This was the first, but not the last time that Shimon was called contrary. The adjective pursued him all his life. It is interesting that for many years Shimon was self-conscious about his unorthodox opinion concerning Bialik's famous poem. Only thirty years later, when he was already in America, did he hesitantly suggest his views to Avrom Liesin, and the aged poet was greatly excited. "That's just what I have been saying! It slanders the Jews! Did you really say this when you were still a boy? Strange! I wrote the same thing, and, of course, people said it was out of envy."

Shimon never succeeded in locating Liesin's article and he does not know whether Liesin really wrote such a piece.

One Monday after the studies had been finished, Reb Getzel said to Shimon: "You know Nissel, who works for your brother-in-law? I heard that he is the real boss among those people. Tell him quietly that I want to talk to him, and bring him here late tonight, after *Ma'ariv*. Tell him it's a secret meeting."

When Shimon came home he found Nissel washing himself outside in the yard. Nissel had a standard routine. He would fill the large copper jug with water and put it on a chair next to the basin. First he soaped his hands and face and rinsed them in the basin, then he poured the jug of water over his head and shook his mop of hair vigorously, like a colt coming out of the river. He wiped his face with one towel, and used another to clean carefully behind his ears and in every wrinkle and crevice.

Shimon stood near him as he washed himself and whispered: "Reb Getzel asked me to beg you to come to his house secretly tonight, late."

"What's the matter? He wants to test me?" Nissel joked. "I'm not too good at reading—can't make out anything

262

without the dots. And *kashrus* is not along my line, so why should I go to him?"

"Don't joke," Shimon said earnestly. "If Reb Getzel invites you, he must need you. What are you afraid of? He won't bite you. He must want you for something."

"What business could he have with me?"

"He told me it was a secret, but he asked me to persuade you to come. How can I persuade you?"

"Didn't he drop any hint why he wants to see me?"

"He said it was a secret, and that I should come with you," Shimon insisted.

"All right," Nissel conceded. "I'll go. But as for you, Shimon, you know? You pop up in places where you don't belong; you'll end badly this way."

"Wherever I am, there must be some reason for being there; and as for ending badly, since when are you afraid of a bad end? How many chances do you take?"

Nissel threw the damp towel at Shimon. "You have an answer for everything, and a sharp tongue, too. You'll be one of ours yet—or perhaps not, you're too stubborn. Very well, I'll come, but not with you. I'll be at the old man's."

When Shimon came to Reb Getzel he found Shimshon, Dovid-Arieh's son there. But Nissel hadn't arrived yet. However, he came a few minutes later. Reb Getzel ordered Shimon to serve them tea. The two young men sat silently and waited to hear what the old man had to say. When they finished their tea, the old man addressed them:

"I called both of you because, as I understand, you, Shimshon, are something of a general among your people, and you, Nissel, are the real boss in your crowd. I am not quite clear about what is what in your societies, though I have the impression that you are a bit at each other's throats—a kind of Hasidim and Misnagdim. But now I called you in connection with the trouble that is brewing."

"Rebbe," Nissel interjected, "does the little one have to hear all this?"

"Let him stay," Reb Getzel said. "He is my pupil, and

though he is young, let him listen. One day he will fill my place, and what we say here is a real-life *Emek Habocho*. A Jewish boy should know *Emek Habocho* by heart."

Nissel smiled. "I see you are preparing reserves."

Reb Getzel did not answer Nissel's sarcastic remark. "Yes," he continued, "I called you to talk about the trouble. At such a time Jews have to be prepared for three things; as our father Jacob did: gifts, prayer and war. So far as gifts are concerned, the proper palms have already been greased, and the police officials will be on hand in the market-place. And as for prayer, Yude and the Psalms Sayers Society will attend to that. I did not call you to ask you to talk to the police chief or to recite Psalms. I called you in connection with the third item—war. You, Shimshon, are something of a general, I heard—you deal with pistols; and you, Nissel, give the orders in your society, so I would like to know what is your plan? War doesn't mean simply fighting; there must be a plan and strategy."

"What is there to plan, Rebbe? We have over fifty young men; if all of them had real weapons, we could handle any situation," Shimshon answered. "All the parties are united in this."

"I don't like it, Shimshon," Reb Getzel answered. "Who are the 'them,' and exactly how many are they? It's not clear. You don't even know how many you will have to fight against, and what kind. Will it be plain blackguards, or soldiers, or peasants?"

"If we have enough weapons we can handle any of them," Shimshon said with assurance.

"You are a fool, Shimshon," Reb Getzel said quietly. "Did you handle the situation in Rechitse? Or in Homel?"

"It would have been much worse without the self-defense."

"Maybe, maybe," Reb Getzel agreed, "but the self-defense didn't prevent the pogroms. The prophet Isaiah long ago said about war that it requires both counsel and valor. That means a plan wisely devised."

264

"We plan not to allow the hooligans or the soldiers to come into town," Shimshon said. "We will ambush them at the woods, along the road that leads from the station to town."

"An ambush is not a bad idea," Reb Getzel said taking a pinch of snuff. "But how do you know that the troops will come on the day of the pogrom? Maybe they will come to town a day or two earlier? After all, you won't just simply attack troops. Besides, do you think that with your fifty pistols you can stop a company of regular troops with rifles from entering town?"

"We don't have pistols for all, but if we had, things would not be so bad," Shimshon said courageously.

"So you will get them. All you have to do is approach the richer people in town quietly. Do I have to spell it out for you? But this won't save us."

"Excuse me, Rebbe," Nissel intervened. "Surely you didn't call me to listen to a debate between you and Shimshon. What is your plan, and where do I come in?"

"My plan is to threaten the peasants in the neighboring villages that if they allow a pogrom in town, their villages, and especially their barns will be burned down."

Nissel pondered the matter. "Not a bad plan," he finally conceded. "But how should we go about it?"

"I would like to know, from both of you, how many Christian boys you have in your organizations."

"It's a secret, Rebbe, but their number is considerable."

"Now listen to me, both of you," Reb Getzel said. "I don't mean simply Christian boys. I mean the kind that can be depended upon, not the sort who, in case of a pogrom, will cross themselves and start shouting 'Kill the Jews!'"

Nissel gave the matter some thought. "I think I can guarantee ten such. How about you, Shimshon? But don't count the Deacon's daughter, she is too much of an intellectual."

265

"Let me decide that," Shimshon said. "Our party can supply six dependable Christians."

"Enough, more than enough," Reb Getzel said with satisfaction. "Send them out into the villages and let them warn the peasants that if they permit a pogrom in town, their villages will be set on fire. But don't have them say that the Jews would set the fires. Why cause bad blood between neighbors!"

Nissel rose. "Rebbe," he said, "it is a pity that you are an orthodox old man. You would make a fine member of our central committee."

Reb Getzel also rose. "What did you think? That all the wisdom is in young heads? Don't you remember what happened to Rehoboam when he listened to the advice of his young counselors?"

Shimshon and Nissel laughed. "Now we know where this little one gets a verse for every occasion."

There was no pogrom in Kalinkovich. On the day of the Fair, the peasants from the nearby villages came and formed a ring around the town. The afternoon train brought some thirty hoodlums from Homel and Rechitse; but the peasants did not let them enter town. They kept them at the station; they treated them to liquor; and when the evening train came, they loaded them back into the cars and saw them depart. The Fair proceeded along its normal course.

Hasidim in town maintained that Kalinkovich escaped a pogrom because long ago the town had been blessed by the old Rabbi of Stohlen that no evil may befall it.

Shimon became *Bar Mitzvah* on the Sabbath after Tisha b'Av (Shabbos Nachmu), and this event caused a commotion among the artisans in town. Shimon must get *Maftir*, everyone said, even though it was an established custom that the rabbi was entitled to this honor on Shabbos Nachmu. He will have to forego the honor this time, the artisans argued. He will have enough of these honors in

266

years to come, but Shimon would celebrate his *Bar Mitzvah* only once.

Shimon dreaded his *Bar Mitzvah* and was apprehensive about being called up to the Torah. Not that he didn't know how to recite the *haftorah*. He had done so many times by himself. But he feared that he would confuse the blessings which have to be recited before the reading of the Bible portion and after it. The two blessings were very much alike and differed only slightly. Confronted with the entire congregation at this solemn moment, he was afraid that he would say the blessings in the wrong order, and who would believe him that it was only a result of his stage fright? He also feared the shame of such confusion. He was famous all over town for having studied all the six Orders of *Mishnaios* three times, for knowing three tractates of the Talmud, and for knowing the Scriptures. His entire reputation would be ruined by such a simple blunder as confusing the blessings when called up to the Torah.

The rabbi renounced his right to *Maftir* and it was given to Shimon. Though he was ashamed to do so, Shimon took his *Humesh* when he was called up to the Torah, and opened it to the page where the blessings were. Thus encouraged, he did not blunder and went through the ceremony with flying colors. When it was over, all the artisans crowded about him to congratulate him. Zalman Hooman pounded his back and exulted: "You gave out with an *haftorah*, first class. Now your father will have to stand us a drink, the real thing. But tell me, Shimonke, what were you so flustered about when you were called up? Were you afraid you'd confuse the blessings? Not a scholar like you!"

Shimon smiled and did not know what to say. Zalman Hooman had guessed right. To this day Shimon is haunted by a dread of forgetting the simplest words. In fact, he frequently does forget them. His notebooks are filled with scores of definitions of the very simplest expressions. He seldom forgets important matters, but the little things elude his memory.

31. *Two Verses from Isaiah*

That winter Shimon felt lonesome in Reb Getzel's heder. Moishe-Dovid left to study at the *yeshivah* in Lida; Aaron-Moishe went to study by himself in the synagogue, though he actually wasted more time than he spent at study. Beinush and Isroel-Moishe began to study Russian. The new pupils in Reb Getzel's heder were young boys of eleven or twelve. Reb Getzel was aware of Shimon's sense of forlornness and urged him to go to a *yeshivah*. "Your friends have gone away," he said. "Moishe-Dovid went to Reines' *yeshivah* in Lida. I don't know whether he went there to continue his studies, or if it was only an alibi to give him an opportunity to study secular wisdom. You still want to study, though who knows how long you will remain with the *Gemora*. So learn whatever you can now. If you will fill yourself with *Gemora* and its commentaries now, you may in later years have something to return to."

Shimon confided to Reb Getzel: "Mother won't be able to send me anything when I am in a *yeshivah*. Shlomo is getting older and needs a more expensive teacher, and the girls, too, have to study, and times are bad. Even the cow didn't calve this year."

"In cases like this," Reb Getzel reassured him, "Jews have the custom of 'eating days.' You are not so pampered here either."

"But that would mean charity," Shimon protested, "and we always avoided it."

" 'Eating days' is not charity. It is part of the Jewish way of life. For instance, I heard that abroad there are rich people who will their wealth to universities, or they support some students. Among us it is the custom that everybody helps young people who want to study. It's nothing to be ashamed of; all the great men in Israel 'ate days.' "

"In that case, where should I go?"

"Aren't there enough *yeshivos*? Go to Mir, or Slobodka, or Telz. Write to them and they will advise you. I will give you a good letter of recommendation."

Shimon decided to write, but for some time he couldn't strike the right tone. Week followed week and still he didn't write to a *yeshivah*. "It will get too late," he scolded himself, and still he didn't write. He felt suspended in a void. By sheer chance Shimon in the end went to the *yeshiva* in Kremenchug. The choice was made in a strange way.

Reb Mordecai Kroll had come to Kalinkovich years before as the prized son-in-law of one of the outstanding families. Reb Mordecai had all the admired virtues—he was a scholar, a good speaker, and came from one of the best families in the region. He was accomplished in every respect.

At this time the people of Kalinkovich were all excited about the elections to the Duma. The Jews of Kalinkovich were not too anxious to take the trouble to travel a third time to the county seat to cast their ballots. It's a game not worth bothering with, they said; they elect a Duma, and dismiss it, then elect another one, and dismiss that one. What is that fool in Petersburg trying to accomplish? Provide business for the railroads?

But Mordecai Kroll had a high opinion of the importance of the Duma. On Friday before the elections, notices were posted in all the three houses of prayer that on Saturday Mordecai Kroll would deliver a speech that would last not more than a few minutes—he would discuss two verses in the Scriptures which had contemporary significance. Naturally everyone was curious, and on Saturday afternoon the synagogue was packed.

Mordecai Kroll kept his promise. He ascended the platform wrapped in his *tallis* and addressed his audience. "You probably thought," he began, "that I would again speak about the elections to the Duma. Not at all. I will not mention the elections with a single word. Today I want to give you my interpretation of verses thirteen and fourteen from Isaiah, chapter twenty-one.

"The prince of the prophets, Isaiah, stood on the steps of the Temple and called: 'Come, people of Judah, and I will bare my prophecy, The Burden of Duma.' Duma is the same as Edom, as Rashi explained it. And the prophecy? 'God called to me from Seir, Watchman, what of the night?' Edom is troubled. The capitol of Edom calls twice to the watchman to find out what of the night, for there is some turbulence in the East. Could it be the dawn? Then the watchman in his tower would be the first to discern it. The watchman answers: 'Morning is come, and also the night.' Though dawn is coming, it is still night. A better interpretation would be, Day is indeed coming, but it is sure to be followed by night again; therefore do not neglect your duties while you have the light.

"But our Jews," he continued, "are tired of this game, these constant changes from day to night. 'What can we do,' they argue, 'when the decisions are made far away and they are not in our hands?' However, *Metsudat David* already declared, 'Forever be on guard!' Without constantly being on guard, a great misfortune may come. Only God knows the secret of the future, but man is bound to do his duty. As *Midrash Tanhuma* states: 'Man must not say, I will eat and drink and enjoy myself, and Providence will have mercy. No, man must labor with all his might, and then God will bestow His blessing. Whether the dark of night will return again or not, we must do our duty, and by virtue of this the redeemer will come to Zion, and say Amen."

270

He finished and descended from the platform, and the entire congregation pressed around him to congratulate him. Shimon also liked the speech, but he stood aside. That was ever his way. He sometimes thinks that it is the way of pride and not of modesty. Only later, after *Minhah*, when he found Mordecai Kroll alone in the synagogue engrossed in a book, did Shimon go up to him and congratulate him. Mordecai gave the customary answer and looked at him carefully.

"You are Yerucham's boy, Shimon, aren't you? I heard about you. I was told that you are the stubborn kind, and that in your studies you like to follow your own system. Is it true that you have studied by yourself all the six Orders of the Mishnah?"

Shimon admitted that he had done so, and Mordecai Kroll asked him to recite a complicated passage. Shimon was displeased at first. Why the sudden test? he wondered. But it would not have been courteous to refuse and he took the appropriate folio and recited the requested passage and quoted all the commentaries on it. Mordecai Kroll listened appreciatively.

"Reb Getzel deserves congratulations," he said when Shimon had finished. "You must have wondered why I asked you to recite. (Suddenly he began addressing Shimon in the more formal plural "you" instead of the former "thou".) Some time ago I received a letter from my friend Reb Moishe, the prodigy of Volozhin, that he was opening a *yeshivah* in Kremenchug. What the ignoramuses of the South need a *yeshivah* for I do not know. But Reb Moishe always had his own system in study. He is now looking for suitable pupils, and it seems to me that you would be right for him. If you agree, I will write him a letter this very evening.

It was agreed that Shimon should go to the *yeshivah* in Kremenchug—by wagon as far as Mozir, and then by river boat.

One warm spring afternoon, a few days before Shimon's departure, he sat with Mother on the steps leading from the corridor to the garden. The mood of the impending separation was upon them, and they talked quietly.

"A few more days," Mehre sighed, "and you will go away. The house will feel empty. You are still so young, and now you go to live among strangers. But deep in my heart I envy you. Azarich is the farthest I ever got from Kalinkovich. Our sort is like a tree—rooted in the ground. We get into a rut and we are stuck there. You are lucky—you are getting away. How I wanted to escape this poor house, and to get away from this life! The world is so big and beautiful! But where could a simple girl like me go? I can't even sign my name! What could I do? Become a servant! If I had been a man, at least! But luck is with you and you are escaping. You are going away to study. You will become a scholar and I will be proud of you."

"But, Mother," Shimon said, "It may turn out that I shall abandon the Torah, as so many do nowadays, and then you will grieve instead of being proud."

"If you change your ways because you decide that there is something higher then Torah, I will not grieve. Anyway, it's not only students who become *apikorsim*. You think I don't know that Simcha stopped saying his prayers? All the tailor and shoemaker apprentices stopped saying their prayers. Does that mean that they have become so smart overnight? No, if one must stop praying, it is better to study and to know why one shouldn't pray."

"Mother, you are wise, wiser than many famous scholars," Shimon couldn't help admiring her reasoning.

"What use is my wisdom?" Mehre complained. "What good has it done me? Wisdom alone is not enough; one must also study to know what to do with it. But here I go talking nonsense about last year's snow, when I should encourage you, now that you are going away and you will have to eat at strangers' tables and depend on charity."

"It won't be charity, Mother. Reb Getzel is right. It is

an old Jewish custom to 'eat days.' Some of the greatest
men in Israel 'ate days,'" Shimon repeated his Rebbe's
words.

"It were better if I could send you enough money for
your support," Mehre insisted.

"Many things could be better. But should I remain here
just because you can't afford to support me away from
home? I am not better than others, and it won't harm me
to 'eat days' as thousands of other Jewish boys do."

"You are right, my son," Mehre agreed. "You talk like
a grown-up. For, look at it another way, didn't your father
suffer when he was a shoemaker's apprentice? And then
the humiliations that an apprentice has to stand in a shop!
Yet what did he get out of it? If one must suffer hardship
and humiliation, at least let it be for the sake of learning.
But there is one thing I want you to remember after you get
to be a rabbi, or a doctor, or an author—don't forget that
there are many shoemakers in the world, and that they,
too, deserve something."

"Mother," Shimon answered sadly, "you're already
making me a rabbi, or a doctor, or an author; but I am
only thirteen years old, and I go to a *yeshivah*, and I will
have to 'eat days.'"

"My heart tells me so," Mehre mused. "When you were
still a little one, and couldn't walk, I already knew what
you would become. Some day you will recall what I now
say to you."

"I hope your words will come true," Shimon added
piously.

"They will come true," Mehre said confidently. "Now
let us go inside and have some tea. It is getting chilly."

After Passover, Zalman Hooman took Shimon to Mozir.
As soon as the wagon left town, Zalman said, "Come,
Shimonke, sit here alongside me. I feel kind of low that
you are going away, as if you were my own son."

Shimon climbed up to the driver's seat and sat near

Zalman. A while later, when they passed the first village, Zalman spoke: "Do you remember, Shimon, when I brought you the first *Gemora*? Remember how you recited for me from it?"

"Yes."

"Do you remember which part?"

"Yes, the first Mishna in *Berakhot*."

"Now, if you want to be a good boy, you will do it all over again, the same part, with the same tune, and then I will feel that I have a direct share in you."

Shimon smiled. "When does one recite *Shema* in the evening?" he began.

The horses plodded along, and Zalman lowered his head into his collar. Shimon saw tears roll down Zalman's face, and he stopped.

"Reb Zalman," he said, "it's not nice! Even Mother didn't cry when we parted."

Zalman whipped the horses. "Who's crying? Some dust got into my eyes."

When they came to Mozir, Zalman took Shimon's trunk to the ship and found him a comfortable place. At parting he instructed him: "And now, Shimon, you have to give me your word of honor that you will write your mother the exact day and hour when you will be coming back from the *yeshivah*; I want to meet you, whether it's at the train or at the boat."

He took Shimon's hand, pressed it, and folded the fingers into a fist, then he ran off the ship. When Shimon opened his tightly closed fist, there was a three-ruble note in it.

The steamer blew its horn. Shimon's eyes filled with tears. In his heart he prayed: "It is such a burden to carry! Help me, God, that they shouldn't be ashamed of me!"

Slowly the steamer moved from the dock.

THE END

274